# Achieve
# IELTS 2

## English for International Education

## Workbook

**Louis Harrison**
**Caroline Cushen**
**Susan Hutchinson**

**mc Marshall Cavendish**
Education

NO CD

Marshall Cavendish Education
119 Wardour Street
London W1F 0UW
www.mcelt.com/ielts

Editorial, design and production by Hart McLeod, Cambridge

Printed and bound by Times Offset (M) Sdn. Bhd. Malaysia

## Acknowledgements

The Authors and Publishers would like to acknowledge the following sources from which extracts in the book, as stated, have been adapted.

**Text**

p.15, tx.essortment.com/goldstandards_rgvh.htm, encyclopedia.laborlawtalk.com/Fiat_currency, en.wikipedia.org/wiki/Money, www.ex.ac.uk/~RDavies/arian/llyfr.html; p.21, www.littleviking.org.uk/travel/offers.htmlwww.youngpersons-railcard.co.uk; p.22, www.budapesthotels.com/touristguide/bkv.asp; p.29, based on article from New Scientist Creepy crawlies to explore other worlds, 23 July 2005; p30, based on article from Newsweek The future of entertainment, 26 September 2005; p.35, en.wikipedia.org/wiki/Milton_Keynes_(borough); p.38 www.archiseek.com/guides/spain/catalunya/barcelona; p.43, Adventures in English by Melvyn Bragg, 2003; p.59, www.bbc.co.uk/education/asguru/generalstudies/society/32trade/trade06.shtml; p.63, www.spartacus.schoolnet.co.uk/REnightingale.htm; p.66, www.arabnews.com/?page=9&section=0&article=54958&d=24&m=11&y=2004; p.70, www.australianorganic.com.au – handbook; p.73, atkins.com/Archive/2001/12/15-217072.printable.html; p.79, based on article from New Scientist A land turned to dust, Caroline Williams, 4 June 2005; p.81, based on article from New Scientist Ten steps to saving the planet Too good to waste – the A-Z of recycling, 10 Sept 2005.

**Photos**

p.7a ©Royalty-Free/Corbis; p.8 t ©Mark Peterson/Corbis, b ©Bob Krist/Corbis; p.9 ©Frank Chmura/Alamy; p.10 ©Photofusion Picture Library/Alamy; p.14 ©Louis Harrison; p.15 ©Helene Rogers/Alamy; p.17 ©geogphotos/Alamy; p.21 ©Hart McLeod; p.22 a ©Geopix/Alamy, b, d and g ©Louis Harrison. c ©Transport of Delight/Alamy, e ©Matt Fagg/Alamy, f ©Barry Lewis/Corbis, h ©Grant Farquhar/Alamy; p.27 all ©Louis Harrison; p.28 a and c ©Roger Quinn, used courtesy Roger Quinn, Biorobotics Lab,

Case Western Reserve University, b ©NASA, d ©Rob Michelson/GTRI/Science Photo Library, e ©NASA/Science Photo Library; p.30 ©Dimension/Everett/Rex Features; p.32 ©Hank Morgan/University of Massachusetts at Amherst/Science Photo Library; p.35 t-b ©London Aerial Photo Library/Corbis, ©Robert Stainforth/Alamy, ©Robert Stainforth/Alamy; p.37 ©Peter Bowater/Alamy; p.38 t-b ©Dave G Houser/Post-Houserstock/Corbis, ©Archivo Iconografico, S.A./Corbis, ©Patrick Ward/Corbis, ©AM Corporation/Alamy; p.39 l-r ©ImageState/Alamy, ©Altrendo Travel/Getty Images, ©David Wall/Alamy; p.40 t-b ©BL Images Ltd/Alamy, ©David Lawrence/Alamy, ©The Hoberman Collection/Alamy; p.43 t-b ©Yadid Levy/Alamy, ©Gary Edwards/Zefa/Corbis, ©WizData.inc./Alamy, ©image100/Alamy; p.44 ©Hulton Archive/Getty Images; p.50 a ©imagebroker/Alamy, b ©Hart McLeod, c ©Gari Wyn Williams/Alamy, d ©Photofusion Picture Library/Alamy, e ©Helene Rogers/Alamy, f ©Royalty Free/Corbis, g ©Janine Wiedel Photolibrary/Alamy; p.57 ©Reuters/Corbis; p.60 ©Aliki Sapountzi/Aliki Image Library/Alamy; p.63 ©Bettmann/Corbis; p.64 ©Photonica/Getty Images; p.65 ©Royalty Free/Corbis; p.66 ©Reuters/Corbis; p.69 ©William Whitehurst/Corbis; p.70 a ©Dynamic Graphics Group/Alamy, b ©Ingram Publishing/Alamy, c ©Photofusion Picture Library/Alamy, d and g ©Louis Harrison, e ©Richard Hamilton Smith/Corbis, f ©BFA/ACO, used with kind permission; p.73 t ©Becky Luigart-Stayner/Corbis, b ©Royalty Free/Corbis; p.74 clockwise ©Digital Archive Japan/Alamy, ©foodfolio/Alamy, ©Digital Archive Japan/Alamy, ©D. Hurst/Alamy, ©Chloe Johnson/Alamy, ©Nikreates/Alamy; p.79 ©ShelbyImages.com/Alamy; p.81 Mehau Kulyk/Science Photo Library; p.84 ©Tom Stewart/Corbis

The Authors would like to thank Anna Gunn, our editor, for her good advice and guidance, Kriszta Liptak and Guy Harrison for images used in the book, and Kazuyo Mitsuhashi and Hsiao-Pu Chu for help with Unit B.

# Contents

# Map of the book

| Language study | Pronunciation | Study skills |
| --- | --- | --- |
| present tenses | sentence stress | using a dictionary |
| asking for information negatives | word stress | similar and opposite words |
| comparatives and superlatives past simple and past continuous | -ed past tense endings | capitalisation |
| passive and active forms | linked words | keeping vocabulary |
| passive sentences describing changes | /w/ and /j/ between words | speed reading |
| phrasal verbs future forms | words linked with /r/ | grammar notebooks |
| past perfect third conditional | words for crime and criminals | collocation (1) |
| information clauses | defining and non-defining clauses | keeping learning diaries |
| would and used to reported speech | word stress | collocation (2) |
| reporting verbs | final /t/ or /d/ sound | studying effectively |
| phrasal verbs future continuous and future perfect | /əʊ/, /ɔ:/, /ʌ/, /ɒ/ | learning outside class study timetables |
| adjectives for people and things inversion | syllables word stress | test preparation |

# International student

| In this unit you will practise: | |
| --- | --- |
| Study skills | using a dictionary |
| Language study | present tenses |
| Listening | note completion; short answer questions |
| Reading | general training module – matching headings with paragraphs; yes / no / not given |
| Writing | describing charts |

## Study skills: using a dictionary

**1** A good dictionary contains information about the meaning of words, their grammar, pronunciation and different examples of their use. Read the dictionary entry and answer the questions.

---

**deposit¹** /dɪˈpɒzɪt/ **noun [C]**

**1.** a first payment that you make when you agree to buy something expensive such as a car or house. The rest of the money that you pay later is called the **balance**: *She paid a £500 deposit and agreed to pay the balance within six months* • **put down a deposit** (= pay it) *We've put down a deposit on a new house.* **1a.** an amount of money that you pay when you start to rent something such as a flat or car that is returned to you when you stop renting it. **1b.** an amount of money that you pay into a bank account: **make a deposit** *He made a £2,000 cash deposit on 5 April.*

**2.** a layer of metal or another substance that has formed in soil or rock: *Rich mineral deposits have been discovered in the area.* **2a.** a layer of a substance that gradually forms on or inside something: *the build up of fat deposits in the arteries.*

**deposit²** /dɪˈpɒzɪt/ **verb [T]**

**1.** *formal* to put or leave something somewhere: *They deposited their suitcases at the hotel.*

**2.** to pay money into a bank account: *Billions of dollars are deposited in banks every day.* **2a.** to put something valuable in a safe place.

**3.** if a substance is deposited in the soil or in rock, it gradually gathers there and forms a layer: *These sediments were deposited by floods thousands of years ago.*

---

1 Is it an English–English dictionary or bilingual dictionary?
2 Where is the main stress in the word?
3 Is *deposit* countable or uncountable as a noun?
4 Which meaning of the noun *deposit* is about money and which is about minerals like coal or iron?
5 Which new word means *an amount of money to pay later*?
6 Which verbs go together with the noun *deposit*?
7 Can we use *deposit* as a verb without an object?
8 Which definition of the verb *deposit* is about leaving something somewhere?
9 Which use of the verb *deposit* is formal?

# Language study: present tenses

## Present simple and continuous

**1 Choose the correct verb to complete the conversation.**

A: Good morning, how can I help you?

B: I'd like to join the university library, is this the right place? The Welcome pack (1) <u>is saying / says</u> students should go to the Library Reception.

A: Yes, you're in the right place, but I (2) <u>'m having / have</u> to take some details from you before I can issue a library card. Can you tell me your name and student number?

B: My name's Magali and my student number is UB 34009.

A: Magali? (3) <u>Do / Are</u> you <u>come / coming</u> from France?

B: Yes, I'm from Nice. Do you know it?

A: Well, I know whereabouts it is – I (4) <u>am wanting/want</u> to go to France one day. Now, what's your department?

B: I (5) <u>study / 'm studying</u> mobile communications.

A: So, you (6) <u>take / 're taking</u> an engineering course.

B: That's right: Department of Electrical Engineering. I (7) <u>'m doing / do</u> my final year.

A: And (8) <u>do / are</u> you <u>enjoy / enjoying</u> yourself here?

B: Yes, I like it very much, but we (9) <u>'re having / have</u> a lot of work on the course.

A: Now, wait a minute while the machine (10) <u>'s finishing / finishes</u> your card. Here you are.

## Stative verbs

**2 Correct the mistakes.**

1 Carmen's always thinking that I'm with other girls.

2 I'm not understanding the lecturer very well today.

3 A: Where are you going on holiday?
   B: I'm going to the south of Spain. My brother is owning a small cottage there.

4 We're hearing that you're having a party this evening.

5 Economists are believing that interest rates will go down soon.

## Transitive and intransitive verbs

**3 Correct the mistakes.**

1 I didn't catch your last sentence, could you repeat, please?

2 When are you going to start it doing your essay?

3 Bertrand didn't get the attachment to your e-mail. Can you send again?

4 A: Why do you want my lecture notes?
   B: I want because I'd like to read because I was late for that lecture.

5 Okay, is everyone here now? Good, then let's start it. Today we're looking at the role of advertising.

# Present perfect and present perfect continuous

**4 Match the sentences with the meaning.**

1
1 *It's been raining all day.*     A It stopped raining earlier.
2 *It rained all day.*     B It may still be raining.

2
1 *How long have you been studying English?*     A The person is probably still studying.
2 *How long have you studied English?*     B The person is probably not studying.

3
1 *I've been waiting for you for three hours.*     A The person did not stay.
2 *I waited for you for three hours.*     B The person is still there.

**5 Complete the conversations. Use present perfect or present perfect continuous.**

A: Excuse me, can you tell me when the flight is leaving?

B: I'm sorry, but I'm afraid we don't have any information at the moment.

A: But it's three hours late and I (1) _ve been waiting_ (wait) here for five hours.

B: I'm afraid that all I can tell you, madam, is that we (2) _'ve got_ (get) information that the problem (3) _have been_ (solve) and the flights (4) _has left_ (leave) on time for the past hour.

A: Does that mean that my plane will leave soon? I (5) _'ve been making_ (make) an appointment to meet someone in London.

B: I think that it is a good possibility. I (6) _'ve just checked_ (just check) the flight before yours and it's getting ready to leave now.

A: OK, thanks.

A: And now the business news. First the money markets. The dollar (7) _have rised_ (rise) against the Euro throughout the day and the rate is now 1.3 dollars to the Euro. Experts (8) _have_ (predict) that the dollar will rise even further in the next few days. This is due to the price of oil which (9) _gone up_ (go up) since last weekend when OPEC announced a reduction in oil production. Asian business leaders (10) _have_ (arrive) in Singapore to discuss closer economic cooperation. They (11) _'ve been_ (meet) all day today in the Raffles Hotel and are due to finish their discussion anytime now. Our reporter Magdalene Wong (12) _has been_ (wait) outside the hotel. Magdalene, (13) _have_ the leaders _made_ (make) any progress today?

B: Well, we (14) _'ve had_ (have) reports that this morning's discussion on increasing trade between the countries went well, and since lunchtime the leaders (15) _have been_ (talk) about lowering trade barriers between Asian countries.

A: Thanks Magdalene, and we'll come back to this story with an update from Singapore.

# Listening

**1** Listen to a talk and complete the notes. Use no more than three words or a number.

Teaching methods at university

### 1 Lectures
Time: (1) _1 hr_
On some courses there can be (2) _100 or more_ students in a lecture.
Lectures
  a) explain the main points of a topic
  b) (3) _Inter_ for further study
  c) give up-to-date information.
Don't make notes on lecturer's stories, focus on (4) _main point_ and important details.
When making notes, use abbreviations and symbols for (5) _Common_ and terms.
If you do not understand something, (6) _make a book_ to ask afterwards, keep notes from lectures (7) _read_ in a file and review them regularly.
You may like to record lectures on (8) _____ , but ask permission first.
_dg to_

### 2 Seminars
These are (9) _small_ where students and a tutor discuss topics.
The tutor often asks students to prepare (10) _short  coated_ for discussion.
The aim is not to be told a correct answer – the aim is to (11) _Understand_ and make judgements about them. This process helps students to (12) _____ .
Participating is part of the process, so try to (13) _could_ even if this is difficult.

### 3 Tutorials
_But_
Time: (14) _30–40_ minutes
The tutor gives (15) _a y s_ on a piece of work. Try to ask questions about your work or topics from (16) _____ and seminars.
_Lectures_

**2** Listen again and answer the questions.

1 On courses with only a few hours of classes, how should students work? _Make a note  IS long  understand_
2 Apart from the three methods mentioned above, what are the other three teaching methods?
3 In lectures, when do students usually ask questions?
4 What are seminars meant to encourage?
5 Why do some international students find seminars frightening?
6 What are tutorials?

# Pronunciation

**1** Listen and underline the stressed words.

*it's essential to go to lectures*
*It's really important to go over your lectures*
*Working independently is crucial at university*

**2** Listen again and practise.

# Reading

IELTS tasks: general training module – matching headings with paragraphs; yes / no / not given

**◘ Read the passage and match the headings with the paragraphs.**

1 style of education
2 voluntary work
3 finding accommodation
4 getting involved at university
5 leisure time
6 nightlife
7 adapting to a different culture
8 taking part in sports

## UNIVERSITY SIX MONTHS ON

**A** It only seems like yesterday that I left home but it's already been six months. How time flies! Since I came here, I have not only learned a lot about Britain's culture, but also made a lot of friends from all over the world. Even more importantly, my experience here has
5 inspired me a lot and positively changed some of my perspectives. My studies have been going really well and I love my new course. Fitting in has been a major issue because my culture, food and background are completely different from everyone else. Still, I love these differences because it means that I have so much to learn.

**B** 10 I really enjoy the intellectual atmosphere here as I can freely express my own views. I have always been taught to accept all information taught in textbooks, and the teacher was always right, there was no room for arguments or disagreements. I just had to accept and memorise facts. However, at the university, lecturers have a role in
15 the development of my own thoughts and ideas. In fact, arguing and debating with tutors is encouraged, to promote independent thinking. My professor always encourages us to challenge his views or traditional thinking in class – students in Britain are encouraged to think critically.

**C** 20 As a former journalist, I am amazed at the degree of independence and freedom that the media enjoys here in Britain. It is very easy to read or hear different points of view from the media. In such a relaxed atmosphere, I volunteered to be a student representative at the Students' Union, participating actively in student union meetings and raising various issues concerning student rights. We successfully changed our school's decision to cancel one of our modules. I also sent an e-mail to the Head of the Business School, suggesting a
25 better way of running our course, and the Head has promised to reply. Now, I have learned not only to be more confident to talk about my views but also to be more open to consider different opinions.

**D** Now I would also like to tell you about my busy social life outside my studies. I am now teaching children in the city, although I am not being paid for this work. With my help, not only are their language and writing skills improving but also their bonds to Chinese culture are strengthened. Also I often help the elderly people of Bristol. I helped them
30 arrange a party and invited a group of local primary school children to join.

**E** Besides academic studies at university, there are numerous extra-curricular activities that I have participated in. This made me realise that as a student, the United Kingdom has much to offer. Although I am very busy, I have still managed to visit a lot of British cities even though the weather is colder here than the inside of a fridge. I find that Britain has a great sense of history and culture, which is in its own way as rich and varied as my country's.

**2** Read the passage again. Do the statements reflect the claims of the writer? Write ...

**YES** if the statement reflects the claims of the writer.
**NO** if the statement contradicts the claims of the writer.
**NOT GIVEN** if it is impossible to say what the writer thinks.

1 Studying abroad has changed the writer's opinions in a good way.
2 Tutors in this country like students to follow traditional thinking.
3 It is very easy to become a student representative.
4 The writer does a lot of things when she is not studying.
5 The writer thinks that the UK is less historically interesting than her own country.

**3** Read the passage again and answer the questions.

1 Which three things are different from the student's country?
2 What does the student enjoy at university and why?
3 What school decision did the student change?
4 Which two volunteer activities does the student do?
5 What else does the student do besides studying at university?

# Vocabulary

**1** Complete the mind map. Use the words in A.

| A | |
|---|---|
| eligible | enthusiastic |
| organised | spoilt |
| applicant | bright |
| lazy | grant |
| intelligent | hardworking |
| fund | |
| independent | |

1 _____     6 _____

2 _____     **good**     5 _____

3 _____     4 _____

**characteristics of international students**  —  **International Studies**  —  **finance**

1 _____     2 _____

4 _____     3 _____

**bad**

1 _____     2 _____

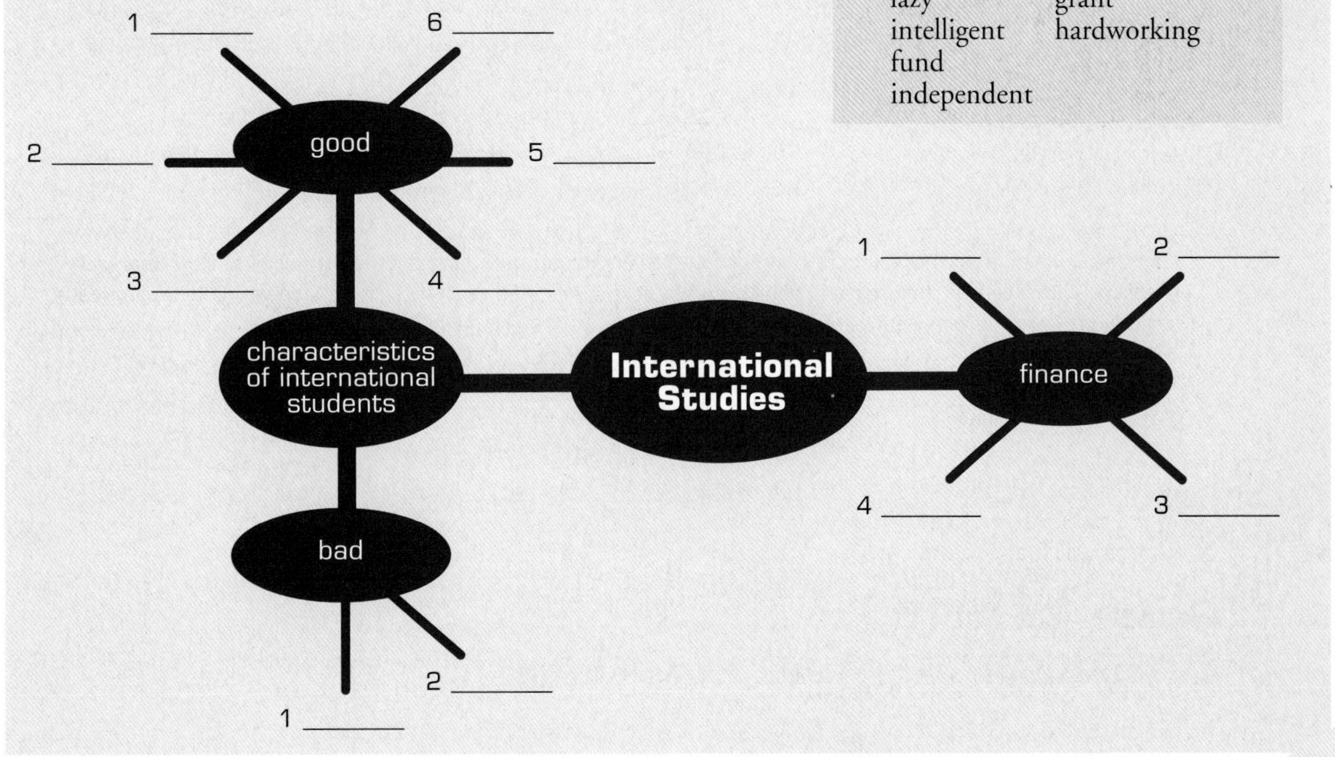

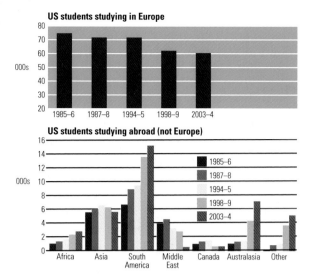

US students studying in Europe

US students studying abroad (not Europe)

1985–6
1987–8
1994–5
1998–9
2003–4

# Writing

**1** **Look at the charts and answer the questions.**

1 What does the first chart show?

2 What general statements can you make about the information in the second chart?

3 Are these statements true or false?

   a The number of American students in Europe rose steadily.

   b The number of American students in South America rose slightly.

   c The number of American students in the Middle East declined slowly.

**2** **Complete the report. Use the phrases in B.**

**B** very dramatic rise
in general
bar charts
long term trend
remained quite
  constant
declined
between 1985
  and 2004
overall number
climbed

The (1) _____ show the number of students from the USA studying abroad (2) _____ . The first chart shows the number of students going to study in Europe and the second chart shows the number of American students studying in the rest of the world. (3) _____ , we can see a (4) _____ in the movement of American students away from countries in Europe and the Middle East in favour of studying in countries in South America and Australasia.

In 1985–6, the number of students from the United States studying in Europe was approximately 75,000, but by 2003–4 this had (5) _____ by over 10,000 to 60,000 students. In contrast, American students going to study in South America (6) _____ from around 7,000 to approximately 15,000 – a 100% increase, and in Australasia from 1,000 to nearly 7,000, a (7) _____ . If we look at American students studying in Asia, we can see that numbers have (8) _____ at around 6,000.

In conclusion, we can see from the charts that although the (9) _____ of American students studying abroad has been rising, their destinations for education have changed.

## Revise for IELTS

**Can you remember the test advice in *Achieve IELTS*?**

1 What information in reading passages can help you to predict the topics in a passage?

2 How can predicting what a reading passage contains help you answer the questions?

# Money

## Study skills: similar and opposite words

1 A good way to increase your vocabulary is to learn words with similar and opposite meanings. Complete the table with similar words. Use the words in A.

| word | similar word(s) | opposite word(s) |
|---|---|---|
| correct | *right* | *incorrect / wrong* |
| expensive | 1 _____ | 6 _____ / *cheap* |
| install | 2 _____ | 7 _____ / *remove* |
| ability | 3 _____ | 8 _____ |
| place | 4 _____ | 9 _____ |
| responsible | 5 _____ | 10 _____ |

2 Complete the table with the opposites of the words in column 1. Use *in-* (x2), *un-*, *mis-*, *ir-*.

**In this unit you will practise:**

| | |
|---|---|
| Study skills | similar and opposite words |
| Listening | note completion; short answer questions |
| Reading | classifying; true / false / not given |
| Language study | asking for information; negatives |
| Writing | general training module – a letter of application; referring to numbers |

**A** in charge
put in
capability
dear
locate

## Listening

**IELTS tasks: note completion; short answer questions**

3 1 Listen to a conversation and complete the form.

3 2 Listen again and answer the questions.

1 Where does the student find the course code?

2 How much is the fee if the student pays by monthly instalments?

3 In what situation can the student get some money back?

4 What details does the student need about the university for the bank?

**Payment of fees**
course fees ☑ accommodation fees ☐ both ☐

**Course details**
school of *managements* department of *mauketing*
course: short course ☐ part-time ☐ full-time ☑
undergraduate ☐ postgraduate ☑
MA ☑ MBA ☐ MSc ☐
course code: *PMK IMAN*
payment type:
credit card ☐ direct debit ☑ cash ☐ cheque ☐

**Student details**
Name: _____ University number *UB606 B3*
*PerJensen*

# Reading

**❶ Read the passage and classify the descriptions as referring to …**
- **commodity money (CM)**
- **representative money (RM)**
- **fiat money (FM).**

1 _____ is influenced by supply and demand.

2 _____ uses the gold standard.

3 _____ depends upon the promises of governments.

4 _____ is a form of money that has no value as a physical object.

5 _____ only has value if people believe they can use it for trade.

6 _____ has been used for thousands of years.

**❷ Read the passage again. Do the statements agree with the information given? Write …**

**TRUE if the statement is true according to the passage.**
**FALSE if the statement is false according to the passage.**
**NOT GIVEN if the statement is not given in the passage.**

1 Economics were the most important reason in the development of money.

2 Pepper was used as money.

3 Different societies have different ways of valuing gold.

4 Notes and coins had value because the government promised to change them for valuable metal like gold or silver.

5 The role of silver in today's economy is very small.

6 Many currencies in Western countries became fiat money when the Euro was introduced.

# THE EMERGENCE OF MONEY

**A**  Money is common to all human societies. However, money did not have a single origin but developed independently in many different parts of the world. A definition of money cannot be based on its physical form and can only be defined by its functions. Money is used as a measurement of value, it functions as a medium of exchange and it also functions as a means of payment. Money can be anything that the parties agree is
5  tradeable. Desirable features of a good basis for money include being able to be stored for long periods of time, transportable (being able to carry it around easily) and difficult to find so that it is worth something. Again, supply and demand play a key role in determining value. Many factors have contributed to the development of money and anthropologists studying primitive money have discovered that economic factors were not the most important. Money in early societies developed as part of religious and social customs such as paying for brides
10  or religious ceremonies. The development of money can be viewed in three basic phases: commodity money, representative money and fiat money.

**B**  Commodity money is made up of objects that are used as a means of commerce such as cowrie shells, whale's teeth, and often cattle. Spices were used as commodity money
15  for a long time – both black and white pepper have been used as commodity money for hundreds of years. In ancient China the cowrie was so important that it became the written symbol for money and the first Chinese coins were made in the form of the cowrie shell. Once a commodity is
20  used as money, it takes on a value that a society adds to it. So although commodity money is real, it should not be seen as having a fixed value in absolute terms. Its value is still socially determined to a large extent. A prime example is

gold, which has been valued differently by many different societies. The value of commodity money can be
25  strongly influenced by supply and demand – the more there is of a particular commodity, the lower its value, but when there is less of it, its value rises. Metals like gold and silver have been used as commodity money for thousands of years, in the form of metal dust, rings, bracelets and other items.

**C**  The system of commodity money in many instances evolved into a system of representative money. In this system, the material that constitutes the money itself had very little value – the money stands for something
30  else. Paper notes and non-precious coins were backed by a government or bank's promise to change it for metal, such as silver. For much of the nineteenth and twentieth centuries, many currencies were based on representative money through the use of the gold standard. The *gold standard* is the use of gold as the standard value for the money of a country. When a country promises to exchange its money for gold it is using the gold standard. The USA and many other Western countries kept the gold standard during the early 1900s. Today,
35  however, gold's role in the worldwide monetary system is very small.

**D**  The next important development of money was fiat money, or floating money. This is a type of currency whose value lies in the fact that a government has made a *fiat*, or promise, that the money is a legal method of exchange. Unlike commodity money or representative money it is not based on another commodity such as gold or silver and is not covered by reserves of gold or silver. Fiat money only holds its value as long as people who
40  have the currency feel that they can find an exchange partner for it at some later time. The value of fiat money lies in being able to use it later as a means of exchange. Most currencies in the world today are fiat money. The move to fiat money happened in 1971 when the USA switched to fiat money. At this time many of the economically developed countries' currencies were fixed to the US dollar and so this single step meant that many of the Western world's currencies became fiat money based. Another example of fiat money is the new,
45  international currency, the Euro. Its introduction changed the face of money, and took over from many of the world's oldest currencies. What is the next step for money? Many people are pointing to e-money, or electronic money, which will mean that money has moved from solid objects to abstract electrical digits.

# Language study: asking for information; negatives

## Asking for information

**1 Put the words in order to make questions.**

1 do *commerce* you how spell?
2 English the of meaning what's *makan* in?
3 do pronounce you *debt* how?
4 you tell me what can means *diş ticaret* in English?
5 repeat could that please you?
6 mean does *paying-in book* what?
7 *well-off* opposite what's the of?
8 is *dollar* another word there for?

**2 Match the questions in 1 with the answers.**

a Yes, of course. I said I wanted to look at your dictionary.
b If you're *well-off* you've got a lot of money, but we say you're *hard up* when you don't have much money.
c It's C-O-double M-E-R-C-E.
d *Ticaret* means trade and *diş* means outside, so together it means *export*.
e It means *eat*.
f We sometimes say *buck*, but it's a bit informal.
g We don't pronounce the *b*, it's pronounced /det/.
h Basically, it's something you use to put money into a bank account.

**3 Write questions for the answers.**

1 Which _____ ? I opened an account with the HSBC.
2 How _____ ? It's £25 to send money overseas electronically.
3 Could _____ ? Yes, the nearest cash point is on Oxford Road.
4 Have _____ ? Here are ten 10p coins in change.
5 What _____ ? The current exchange rate is 105 rupees to one pound.

## Negatives

B
~~im~~ expensive
~~un~~ believable ٦
penny
٤ government ~less
probable
problem

**4 Complete the sentences with the negative of the words in B. Use *un-*, *in-*, *im-*, *-less*, *anti-*, *-free*.**

1 My brother has gone on another demonstration against the prime minister – he's very _____ .
2 You've failed the course again – that's _____ , nobody fails four times.
3 This course book is only £10 – that's quite _____ for this book.
4 Look, read the label: it says this new currency calculator is guaranteed to be _____ , nothing can go wrong with it.
5 It's highly _____ that Jane will agree to giving you any more money – you didn't pay back the last money she gave you.
6 Poor Christine has lost all her money – she's _____ .

# Writing

**1** **Read the letter to Ms Bates and answer the questions.**

1 What is the student's overdraft limit?

2 What has the bank already done and what might the bank do later?

**2** **Read the reply to Mr Appleby and put the sentences in order.**

---

Tuesday 2nd April

Dear Ms Bates

It has been brought to my attention that you have exceeded your overdraft limit of £100 by £50.

As a result of this I have to inform you that you have been charged a further £25 for going over your overdraft limit without agreeing this in advance with your account manager.

I also have to inform you that if the amount is not paid back in full within five working days you will be charged a further £25.

Please contact me if you have any further questions.

Yours sincerely

R Appleby

Student accounts manager

---

Thursday 4th April

Dear Mr Appleby

☐ As the amount was paid back immediately I would be very grateful if you would take back the charge of £25.

☐ With thanks

☐ I went over my overdraft limit of £100 on Friday evening as I had to pay for a taxi from the city centre back to the campus as this is much safer than walking home alone.

☐ I was very disappointed to find that I had been charged £25 when I received your letter yesterday.

☐ However, I paid back the amount on Monday as soon as the bank was open in the hope that I would not be charged for exceeding my overdraft limit.

☐ Please accept my apologies for exceeding my overdraft limit.

Ms Norma Bates

---

**3** **Read the title and underline the key words.**

*You had to pay your university course fees last week. Unfortunately you are still waiting for money to arrive in your new bank account from your home country. The university has written to you asking for immediate payment, saying they have charged you extra because of the delay. Write a letter to the university. Explain what has happened and tell them what you want to do about it.*

**4** **Write the letter. Use words, phrases and expressions from activity 2.**

# Referring to numbers

**5** **Look at the charts and answer the questions.**

1 What is the main reason for students working?
2 What is the least important reason for students working?
3 How could students save the most money?
4 What percentage of students think working affects their studies?

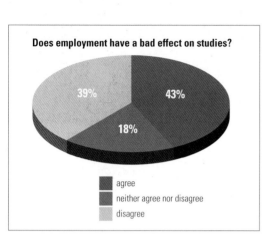

Does employment have a bad effect on studies?

43%
39%
18%

- agree
- neither agree nor disagree
- disagree

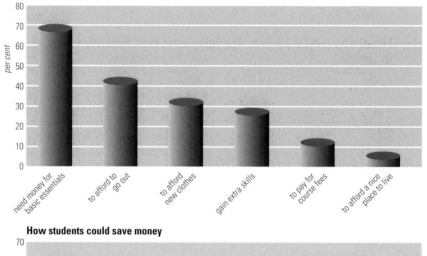

Reasons why students work

per cent

need money for basic essentials · to afford to go out · to afford new clothes · gain extra skills · to pay for course fees · to afford a nice place to live

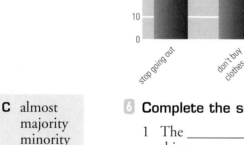

How students could save money

per cent

stop going out · don't buy clothes · don't use mobile phone · cheaper accommodation

**C** almost
majority
minority
over
third

**6** **Complete the sentences. Use the words in C.**

1 The _____ of students needed to earn money for essential things.
2 Just _____ 40% of students used the money from working to go out.
3 However, _____ 60% of the students said they could save money by not going out.
4 Related to going out and meeting people, over one _____ of students said they could save money on mobile phones.
5 At 18%, a _____ of students neither agreed nor disagreed that work affected their education.

**7** **Summarise the information in the tables in activity 5 by selecting and reporting the main features and making comparisons where relevant.**

# Vocabulary

**Complete the crossword and find the missing word.**

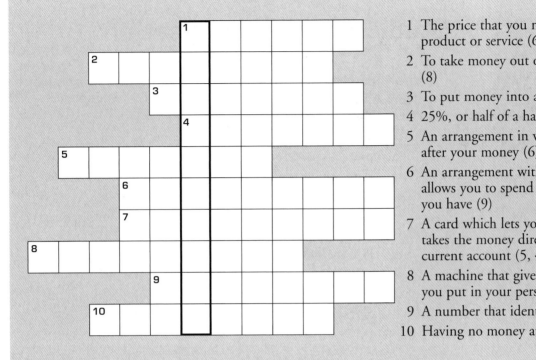

1 The price that you must pay for a product or service (6)
2 To take money out of a bank account (8)
3 To put money into a bank (7)
4 25%, or half of a half (7)
5 An arrangement in which a bank looks after your money (6)
6 An arrangement with a bank that allows you to spend more money than you have (9)
7 A card which lets you buy things and takes the money directly from your current account (5, 4)
8 A machine that gives you money when you put in your personal number (4, 5)
9 A number that identifies a bank (4, 4)
10 Having no money at all (8)

# Pronunciation

**Put the words in D into groups.**

1 ☐☐ *bankrupt*   2 ☐☐ *account*

**4 2 Listen and check your answers.**

**4 3 Listen again and practise.**

> **D**  transfer    payment
>    exchange   bankrupt
>    convert    withdraw
>    statement  account
>    balance    purchase

## Revise for IELTS

**Can you remember the test advice in *Achieve IELTS*?**

1 How can recognising negative prefixes and suffixes help you in the reading and listening tests?
2 What do you receive marks for in writing test task 1?
3 How can giving reasons and opinions for the information in writing test task 1 affect your score?

# Transport

| In this unit you will practise: | |
|---|---|
| Study skills | capitalisation |
| Reading | general training module – yes / no / not given |
| Listening | matching; multiple-choice questions |
| Lanugage study | comparatives and superlatives; past simple and past continuous |
| Writing | part 1 – comparison and contrast |

## Study skills: capitalisation

It is important to remember in your writing the words which begin with a capital letter in English. Match examples 1 – 10 with a – j.

| | | | |
|---|---|---|---|
| 1 | the Mediterranean, the Pacific | a | names of rivers |
| 2 | Chinese, Russian, Mongolian | b | names of countries |
| 3 | the Nile, the Danube | c | acronyms (abbreviations) |
| 4 | the Hilton, the Ritz | d | island groups |
| 5 | Venezuela, Portugal | e | nationalities and languages |
| 6 | Bugis Street, Shaftesbury Avenue | f | mountains and mountain ranges |
| 7 | the USA, the PRC, the USSR | g | names of hotels |
| 8 | the Andes, Mount Everest | h | names of cities |
| 9 | the West Indies, the Philippines | i | names of oceans and seas |
| 10 | Sydney, London, New York | j | names of roads |

## Reading

**IELTS tasks: general training module – yes / no / not given**

Read the passage and write ...
**YES** if the statement agrees with the information.
**NO** if the statement contradicts the information.
**NOT GIVEN** if there is no information about this in the passage.

1 The railcard gives you a 33% discount on any train journey.
2 Only students can apply for this railcard.
3 If you are over 26, you need an ISIC card to apply.
4 You can only use the card for one journey.
5 *Rough Guide* travel books are supplied with your railcard.
6 The card can be used on coaches and ferries.
7 You can get a railcard from the Students' Union.
8 You cannot use the London Travelcard during the rush hour.
9 You can save more if you buy your ticket early.
10 Student telesales can find you the cheapest tickets.

# SPECIAL STUDENT DISCOUNTS

**A** Do you know how to spend less on rail travel? Buy a Railcard! Save one third on most rail fares and you'll have more to spend on the important things in life. Do you qualify? You do
5 if you're a student or aged 15 – 26.

**B** If you are under 26 and applying for your first railcard, you'll need to take proof of age such as a birth certificate, driving licence or passport to your local train station or recognised travel
10 agent, along with a passport photo and £20. Stations and agents accept cash, cheques, debit, credit and charge cards or postal orders. You should receive your Young Person's Railcard within 14 days.

**C** If you're aged 26 or over, you'll need to provide proof that you're a full-time student at a recognised school or college. This has to be over 15 hours a week and for at least 20 weeks in the
15 year. You can either show an ISIC card or have the 'Mature students only' section of the application form completed and certified by your institution.

**D** At just £20 a year, a Young Person's Railcard can pay for itself in just one or two trips. On just one ticket costing £64, for example, you could save £21.33, which more than pays for your rail card. Then you continue to make savings every time you use it.

**E** 20 Looking for inspiration? Wondering where to go and what to do? Check out *Rough Guides* travel books. With information on nine cities across Britain you'll be spoilt for choice.

**F** Travel by rail, by road or by sea. Sail to the Isle of Wight, Eire or Northern Ireland, or visit the capital. Your railcard discount also applies to tickets which include the London Off-Peak Day Travelcard. That way you can travel around on tubes and buses too. You will find you can save a
25 third on most ticket types all over Britain including the popular cheap day returns, saver and supersaver fares. You can also use a Young Person's Railcard to buy tickets on many bus and ship links.

**G** Advice and information: you'll find that it's worth booking your ticket for longer distance journeys in advance, as this can help save even more money. Remember, if you need help making
30 the right decision about your journey, just call student telesales on 01334 462345 or e-mail travel@studenttickets.com. We will give you timetable advice, try to get the best fare for you wherever you are going, issue your tickets and always make seat reservations for you at no additional charge. So, just call into your nearest station and take advantage of this opportunity while you can – then enjoy cheaper travel for a whole year.

**A** chairlift
bus
trolley-bus
steam train
train
funicular train
tram
underground train

# Listening

**1** Match the words in **A** with the pictures.

a

b

c

d

e

f

g

h

**5** **2** Listen and number the pictures in the order you hear them mentioned.

**5** **3** Listen again and choose **A – D**.

1 Travel cards can be used …
   A on all types of public transport.
   B all over Hungary.
   C for up to one month.
   D for railway and metro travel only.

2 The Houses of Parliament are …
   A next to the citadel.
   B on the number two tram route.
   C across the river from the main market.
   D not interesting to see.

3 The Metro operates …
   A in the city centre.
   B during the night.
   C to towns popular with tourists.
   D on suburban routes.

4 The funicular is …
   A more expensive than the chairlift.
   B cheaper going down the hill.
   C opposite Castle Hill.
   D used by skiers.

5 The children's railway …
   A is operated entirely by children.
   B goes to the look-out point.
   C goes through the town centre.
   D is 11 km long.

6 A good public transport system can …
   A not be used in most cities.
   B only be used in capital cities.
   C reduce traffic in the city centre.
   D cause congestion and pollution.

# Language study: comparatives and superlatives; past simple and past continuous

## Comparatives and superlatives

**1** Complete the sentences with the comparative or superlative form of words in B.

**B** high
long
tall (x2)
wide

Although Mount Everest has the (1) _highest_ peak in the world, it is not the (2) _tallest_ mountain. This is Mauna Kea in Hawaii, which measures 32,000 feet from base to tip, making it 2,965 feet (3) _taller_ than Mount Everest.

Angel Falls in Venezuela drops 979 metres from Devil's Mountain. This makes it the world's (4) _longest_ waterfall. However, the world's (5) _widest_ waterfall is Khone Falls, which stretches for 10.8 kilometres across the Mekong River, between Laos and Cambodia.

**2** Write the sentences again using *as ... as* or *not as ... as*. You may need to change the adjective.

1 Prague is smaller than Budapest. Budapest _____ .

2 Both Thailand and Vietnam are beautiful. Thailand _____ .

3 Temperatures in Bahrain and Dubai reached 42 degrees today. Bahrain _____ .

4 Tasmania is further away from Singapore than New South Wales. New South Wales _____ .

5 British Airways and Qantas are equally pleasant to fly with. Qantas _____ .

**3** Put the adjectives in C into groups.

1 *more* / *less* + adjective

2 adjective + *−er* or *−est*

3 irregular

| **C** | |
|---|---|
| far | powerful |
| boring | long |
| hot | efficient |
| near | cool |
| expensive | great |
| good | heavy |
| noisy | difficult |
| fast | slight |
| mountainous | economical |
| bad | enjoyable |
| exotic | light |
| pointed | |

**4** Choose an adjective from C and a word or phrase from D and write sentences.

1 bicycle / Ferrari
*A bicycle is much more economical than a Ferrari.*
*A Ferrari is considerably more exciting than a bicycle.*

2 tram / bus

3 Maglev / steam train

4 Shinkansen / Maglev

| **D** | |
|---|---|
| a (little) bit | considerably |
| a great deal | scarcely |
| somewhat | only just |
| (quite) a lot | much |

# Past simple and past continuous

**E** begin
invest
take
cost
put
go
fly
buy
accelerate

**5** Complete the sentences with the past simple forms of the verbs in E.

1 The driver _____ the car into gear and _____ from 0 to 60 kph in under five seconds.

2 Airbus _____ over twelve billion Euros in the A380, which they _____ to construct in 2002.

3 It _____ three years to finish the project.

4 The students _____ an ISIC card before they _____ to India.

5 It _____ too much to go by sea, so I _____ there instead.

**6** Complete the paragraph with the past simple or past continuous form of the verb in brackets.

Last Saturday the sun (1) *was shining* (shine), so I (2) *decided* (decide) to take the train to London. As it (3) *wasn't raining* (not rain), I (4) *didn't take* (not take) my umbrella, and I (5) *left* (leave) my raincoat behind, too. Of course, by the time I (6) *arrived* (arrive) at Waterloo station, it (7) *was pouring* (pour) down! I (8) *got* (get) off the train, but I (9) *didn't leave* (not leave) the station because I (10) *didn't want* (not want) to get wet. A lot of other people (11) *were doing* (do) the same thing, when suddenly we (12) *heard* (hear) an announcement: 'Passengers are informed that all trains will be cancelled this afternoon due to a strike by rail operators. We apologise for the inconvenience.' Everybody (13) *groaned* (groan). After a while, the rain (14) *stopped* (stop) and the sun (15) *came* (come) out again, but I (16) *didn't know* (not know) what to do next. Then I (17) *saw* (see) Ali. What a relief! He (18) *was standing* (stand) by the ticket office, so I (19) *ran* (run) across. He (20) *invited* (invite) me to stay at his flat, which is quite near the station. We (21) *had* (have) a lovely day, and fortunately the trains (22) *were running* (run) normally the next day, so I (23) *got* (get) home without any more problems.

**7** Complete the questions for the writer of the paragraph in activity 2. Use *you*.

1 Why _____ London? *Why did you go to London?*

2 Why _____ umbrella and raincoat?

3 Which station _____ at?

4 Why _____ the station?

5 What _____ other people _____ ?

6 Where _____ Ali _____ ?

7 _____ normally next day?

8 _____ any more problems?

# Writing

**1** **Put the words and phrases in F into groups.**

1 compare    2 contrast

**2** **Look at tables A and B and answer the questions.**

1 What percentage of people have no money to buy a car?
2 What percentage of people feel that public transport is better for the environment?
3 What percentage of people own a car because it gives them more status?

**3** **Complete the passage with expressions from activity 1.**

The tables show reasons why people own a car or travel by public transport.

Write a report for a university lecturer describing the information in the tables.

The first table show reasons why some people prefer to drive.
(1) _____ , the second table shows reasons why others regularly travel by public transport.

The two most popular reasons for owning a car are freedom and independence, with 29% stating this. This percentage is (2) _____ for those who enjoy driving. (3) _____ , the majority of people who use public transport do so because owning a car is too expensive for them. 36% of people say this. (4) _____ , 25% of those in the survey state that they have not passed the driving test. For these two groups, it is not a matter of choice. (5) _____ , 20% of those who travel on public transport do so because they have concerns about the effect that cars have on the environment, so this group choose not to drive whether or not they can.

18% of drivers feel that they need to have a car because they have children. Another practical reason for driving is that it saves time, and 16% said this. (6) _____ , 8% said that they drive a car because it gives them a higher position in society, even though they may not need to drive. Of the remainder who travel by public transport, 12% say they dislike driving, (7) _____ 7% who feel that driving is too dangerous.

On the whole, it seems that most people would prefer to own a car if they could, (8) _____ a minority make a conscious choice to use public transport.

**4** **Write the essay.**

Tables C and D show the reasons why people travel to work by bicycle or by car.

Summarise the information by selecting and reporting the main features, and make comparisons where relevant.

Write at least 150 words.

**F** in comparison with
conversely
on the other hand
in the same way
in contrast to this
compared with
at the same time
on the contrary
the same as
by contrast

### A  Reasons for owning a car

| | |
|---|---|
| Freedom and independence | 29% |
| Enjoy driving | 29% |
| Need it for the children | 18% |
| Saves time | 16% |
| Social position | 8% |

### B  Reasons for using public transport

| | |
|---|---|
| Cannot afford a car | 36% |
| Didn't pass the driving test | 25% |
| Less pollution | 20% |
| Dislike driving | 12% |
| Less dangerous than driving | 7% |

### C  Reasons for cycling to work

| | |
|---|---|
| Health and fitness | 30% |
| Less pollution | 30% |
| No parking problems | 15% |
| No costs | 13% |
| Faster than driving | 12% |

### D  Reasons for driving to work

| | |
|---|---|
| Comfort | 40% |
| Distance to work | 21% |
| Faster than cycling | 14% |
| Need to carry things to work | 14% |
| Safer than cycling | 11% |

# Vocabulary

**G** cockpit
track
hold
railcard
carriage
fuselage
platform
barrier
gate
lounge
check-in
tail fin
wingspan
signals
galley
guard
steward
driver
pilot
waiting room
boarding card

**1** Put the words in G into groups.

   1  air travel    2  rail travel

**2** Complete the sentences with some of the words and phrases from 1.

   1  The Airbus A380 has a massive _____ of around 80 metres.

   2  The passengers were asked to wait in the airport _____ before going to the check-in.

   3  Passengers are requested to stand behind the _____ until a counter is available.

   4  The pilot and co-pilot climbed into the _____ of the fighter plane.

   5  If you have a _____ , you can get a discount on all your tickets for a year.

   6  The train had eight _____ , four of which were first-class only.

   7  There are 104 seats situated in the plane's _____ .

   8  At the _____ , they took his ticket and issued him with a _____ which he had to present to the _____ when he boarded the plane.

   9  A high-speed railway _____ runs from Paris to Lyon.

  10  The train now waiting at _____ 5 is the two twenty-eight to Hastings.

# Pronunciation

**6** **1** Listen to the recording and put the words into groups according to the final sound.

| | | | | |
|---|---|---|---|---|
| 1 travelled | 5 boarded | 9 wished | 13 worked | 17 recorded |
| 2 invited | 6 dropped | 10 sailed | 14 mended | 18 invested |
| 3 climbed | 7 missed | 11 carried | 15 entered | 19 listened |
| 4 arrived | 8 picked | 12 performed | 16 produced | 20 tested |

   1  final sound /t/   2  final sound /d/   3  final sound /ɪd/

**2** The sounds /l/, /m/, /v/, /d/, /iː/, /r/ are *voiced*: there is a vibration in your voice when you say them. The sounds /p/, /s/, /k/, /ʃ/ are *unvoiced*: there is no vibration. Complete the rule for pronunciation of regular past tense endings.

When the final consonant of the verb is:

   1  voiced, the ending is pronounced _____ .

   2  unvoiced, the ending is pronounced _____ .

   3  /t/ or /d/, the ending is pronounced _____ .

## Revise for IELTS

**Can you remember the test advice in *Achieve IELTS*?**

   1  What is *language repair*?

   2  How do we organise essays that compare and contrast information (two ways)?

# Innovation

## Study skills: keeping vocabulary

**1** Label the pictures. Use the words in A.

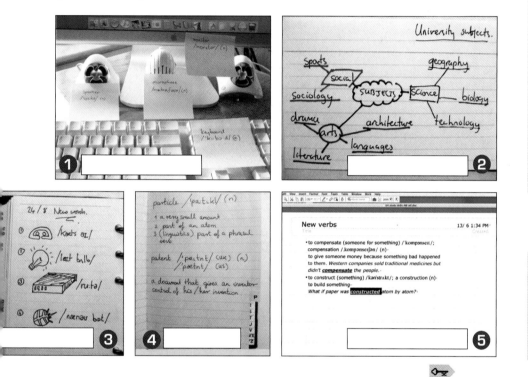

In this unit you will practise:

| | |
|---|---|
| Study skills | keeping vocabulary |
| Reading | general training module – multiple-choice questions; classification |
| Listening | classification; summary completion |
| Language study | passive and active forms |
| Writing | task 1 – describing a process; staging; sequencing |

**A** file cards
post-it notes
laptop
personal
 organiser
notebook

**2** Answer the questions.

1 Which way of keeping vocabulary is organised …
A alphabetically?    C by date?
B thematically?    D by word class?

2 Which way of keeping vocabulary is done …
A with a list?    B with a mind map?    C with pictures?

3 Which information do you need about new words?
A word class (noun / verb / adjective / adverb)
B definition
C translation
D example
E pronunciation
F collocations (words that often go together)

4 How do you practise new words?
A test yourself    B use new words in conversations    C ask a friend to test you

5 How many new words do you learn a week?

6 Which things in 1 – 5 do you do?

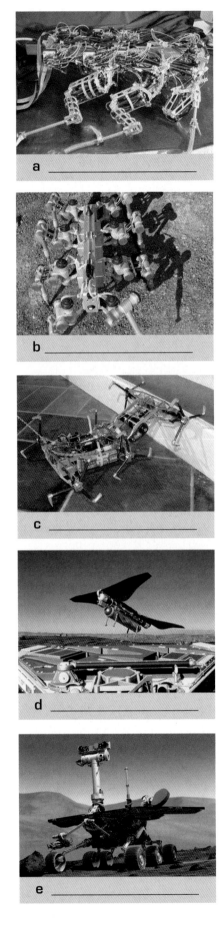

a _____

b _____

c _____

d _____

e _____

# Reading

**1** Read the passage and label the pictures with the names of the robots.

**2** Read the passage and choose A – C.

1 Which robot is on wheels?
   A Scorpion   B Spirit   C Robot V
2 Which creature is not mentioned in the passage?
   A spider   B cat   C moth
3 Which robot has not got six legs?
   A Whegs 2™   B Robot V   C Scorpion
4 Where was Scorpion developed?
   A the United States   B Great Britain   C Germany
5 The passage is taken from a …
   A catalogue.   B magazine article.   C prospectus.

**3** Classify the following descriptions as referring to …

S  Scorpion
O  Opportunity
R  Robot V
W  Whegs 2™
E  Entomopter

**You may use any answer more than once.**

1 _____ can fly.
2 _____ finds it difficult to deal with obstructions.
3 _____ is equipped with a reflex action.
4 _____ performs some tasks better than animals.
5 _____ requires maximum supervision.
6 _____ can sense danger by using antennae.
7 _____ uses up a lot of energy.
8 _____ is currently used on space missions.
9 _____ has similar control systems to a number of different animals.
10 _____ moves in a similar way to a cockroach.
11 _____ has the ability to move underground.
12 _____ risks technological problems due its complex design.
13 _____ tends to follow instructions slowly.

# ROBOTS TO EXPLORE OTHER WORLD

**A** In movies, giant alien insects invade Earth, destroying cities and buildings. Now we humans are hoping to send insect-like robots to investigate the surface of Mars. These 'biomimetic' robots that can walk, climb and fly like real creatures are already under development – and some can almost think like them. Such designs promise to be stronger and more productive than the wheeled vehicles such as NASA's Mars robots *Spirit* and *Opportunity*.
5 Wheeled robots only work when the ground is flat and firm. *Opportunity* has only just freed itself after a month stuck on a 30-centimetre mound of sand. Giving robots the ability to walk like insects with legs makes them far more energetic, allowing them to cope with large obstacles and sandy surfaces.

**B** A six-legged walker inspired by the Death's Head cockroach has been built in the United States. It is called *Robot V* and is twenty times the size of the real-life insect. It was designed to allow the study of legged
10 locomotion over uneven surfaces. But *Robot V*, like most walker designs, has a major problem: it is extremely complicated. Its legs have up to five segments, each one operated by its own artificial pneumatic muscle driven by compressed air. This means it uses a lot of power and has a large number of components that could fail. So the laboratory team developed a design that combines the power of wheels with the agility of legs. The result is *Whegs 2™*, a robot with six wheel-leg hybrids or 'whegs'. Each wheg consists of a central wheel attached to
15 an axle from which three flexible legs stick out, each with its own gripped foot. As the axle turns the wheel, the legs spin round and make contact with the ground. This allows a single motor to drive all six whegs. This keeps its weight and complexity down. The robot can run fast and climb over obstacles like a cockroach. Two forward-facing antennae also allow it to sense whether an object is best avoided, climbed over or tunnelled under.

**C** Conventional robots have other problems too. *Spirit* and *Opportunity*, for example, are remotely controlled from
20 Earth, which involves a wait of up to forty minutes after each command is sent. The hope is therefore to design autonomous explorers that can do some thinking for themselves. With complex six-legged walkers, the task of programming the precisely timed pattern of leg movements is impossibly complicated. So researchers have been turning to biologically inspired control methods.

**D** *Scorpion* is an eight-legged walker being developed in Germany. In animals, groups of neurons called central
25 pattern generators control the rhythmic signal that controls the motors operating in each joint in the leg. *Scorpion* is also equipped with sensors to detect the tilt of its body and the position of every joint on each foot. The information is fed back into the circuits to keep the robot walking smoothly over uneven ground. The software adapts to keep the robot steady over rocks or fine sand. If its sensors feel *Scorpion* starting to lose its balance, they rapidly trigger a pre-programmed 'reflex action' to stabilize it. The team has studied the control
30 systems of a wide range of animals, from cats to stick insects, in order to find the most interesting mechanisms to use for robot movement. One thing *Scorpion* can cope with better than real animals is that when it senses it has fallen over on to its back, the legs invert themselves, allowing it to carry on walking upside down.

**E** A team at the Georgia Tech Research Institute have gone one better than even the most energetic walking robot. It has developed an insect-like flying machine. The robot, inspired by the hawk moth, is called the
35 *Entomopter*. It is designed to fly slowly over Martian surfaces, hover and land on promising spots. Launched from a base station, it can fly off to map the surrounding area, then periodically return to refuel and download data.

# Listening

IELTS tasks: classification; summary completion

⊙ ❶ **Listen to an interview about home entertainment in the future and classify the following descriptions as referring to ...**

L  Lenticular screens.
P  Patio screens.
H  Hologram 3-D screens.

**You may use any answer more than once.**

1  _____ may cause headaches.
2  _____ can be transported out of the home.
3  _____ enable two people to watch different programmes simultaneously.
4  _____ contain a DVD player.
5  _____ give the impression of floating in air.
6  _____ are simple to produce.

⊙ ❷ **Listen again and complete the passage with the words in B.**

**B**  control
depth
downloading
flat
theatre
video games
side and back
image
taking place
wireless

## THE FUTURE OF HOME ENTERTAINMENT

New technologies are changing the way we use media, and the home of the future will be like a personal (1) _____ . The process of (2) _____ will become easier due to high-speed broadband giving us more choice and (3) _____ over what and when we view. Studios will eventually release films, songs and (4) _____ directly to the consumer. There will be changes in how we watch too. 3-D screens will replace (5) _____ screens. This added dimension will enable us to see into the image itself because the hologram screen contains (6) _____ . We will be able to see the action from holographic films as if (7) _____ in front of us. To see 3-D each eye needs to see a different (8) _____ . With a holographic image we can walk around it partly and see (9) _____ views. With patio screens we can take them into the garden as their connection is (10) _____ .

# Pronunciation

❶ **Read the phrases and decide which words are linked.**

*here to tell us more*
*you can even walk part of the way*
*when we talk about dimensions*

⑧ ❷ **Listen and practise.**

# Language study: passive and active forms

**1** **Complete the sentences using the correct form of the words in brackets.**

1 Robots which can walk, climb or fly _____ (call) *biomimetic robots.*

2 With hologram TVs, holographic images _____ (send) into our homes and we _____ (experience) all the action as if is taking place right in our own living rooms.

3 The entomopter robot _____ (develop) by scientists currently.

4 Artists use holography to make pictures which _____ (show) in galleries around the world.

5 Last year, scientists in Japan _____ (develop) a companion robot which _____ (design) to help old people function at home while their children are at work.

6 As technology _____ (grow) we will see the introduction of holographic television.

**2** **Rewrite the sentences so the meaning is the same.**

1 Today, record companies release songs directly to the consumer.
Songs _____ .

2 Studios produce 31 million hours of new TV shows each year.
31 million hours _____ .

3 You can place projection screens throughout the house.
Projection screens _____ .

4 A digital storytelling project was developed by a television company last year.
A television company _____ .

5 The project encourages children to make their own documentaries online.
Children _____

**3** **Make questions from the statements with the words in brackets.**

1 (What / change / new technologies) *What is being changed by new technologies?*
New technologies are changing the way we use television.

2 (Who / the World Wide Web / invent)
The World Wide Web was invented by Tom Berners-Lee.

3 (Who / give / more control and choice)
New technology gives individuals more control and choice.

4 (What / made / slimmer and lighter)
Television screens are being made slimmer and lighter.

5 (Who / give / us more and more choice of programmes)
Television companies are giving us more choice of programmes.

**C**
a 100% reflective mirror
   goes at the other
contains two gases
it begins to glow
the fully reflective mirror
   makes all of the light
   bounce off it
turning it on
forth between the two
   mirrors

# Writing

IELTS tasks: task 1 – describing a process; staging; sequencing

**1** Complete the passage. Use the phrases in C.

# LASERS

Lasers are very simple tools, especially the lasers which are used to make most holograms. A laser is made up of a very thin glass tube, about the size of a drinking straw and (1) _____ – helium and neon. The laser is called a helium-neon laser. The first stage of the process involves connecting the laser to a source of electricity and (2) _____ . Following this, electricity passes through this gas and (3) _____ . In order to get the laser beam out of this tube, two mirrors are placed at both ends of the tube: one partially reflective mirror is placed at one end and (4) _____ . The result is that light begins to bounce back and (5) _____ . The partially reflective mirror lets some of the light pass through and (6) _____ . Finally, the light that passes through comes out as the laser beam.

**2** Underline the passive structures and words and phrases for purpose and sequence in the passage in 1.

**3** Read the question and underline the important words.

> *The diagram shows how a 3D television system works. Summarise the information by selecting and reporting the main features and making comparisons where relevant. You should write at least 150 words.*

**D**
subsequently
the first step
is constituted of
eventually
next
so that

**4** Complete the passage. Use the words and phrases in D.

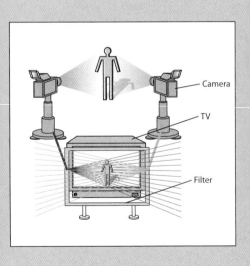

Camera

TV

Filter

The diagram shows a television system which can display 3-D pictures to people sitting in different parts of a room. The system (1) _____ cameras, a screen and a filter which capture a progression of different viewpoints and spread them out into the room with the left view directed to the viewer's left and the right view directed to the right. (2) _____ is to place two TV cameras wider than the human eye to capture left and right views. (3) _____ imaging processing software compares the two images and eight viewpoints are generated that range from the extreme left view to the extreme right. The views are (4) _____ displayed on a television screen. Following this, a filter is fitted to the front of the screen in order to deflect the light from the different slices and spread them out in different directions. It then sends the left image to the left eye and the right image to the right eye (5) _____ the viewer's eyes see slightly different viewpoints wherever they sit. (6) _____ a 3-D effect is created from a wide range of viewing angles.

**5** **Read the passage and underline ...**

1 the overview or general statement about the process.
2 a description of components of the process.
3 a description of the process.
4 words and phrases for purpose and sequencing.
5 passive structures.

**6** **Look at the pictures and write about the process using sentences 1 – 6.**

1 *podcast* = sound recording on Internet
2 need: microphone / computer / sound recording programme / internet connection / MP3 player
3 microphone put into computer, your programme recorded via sound recording program
4 computer connected to Internet, sound file uploaded to podcasting website
5 to listen to programme, computer connected to podcast website through Internet
6 sound file downloaded to computer, sound file transferred to MP3 player

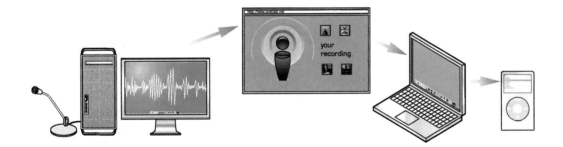

# Vocabulary

**1** **Put the words in E into groups.**

1 related to equipment   2 related to change   3 related to size

| E | crystallise | adapt |
| --- | --- | --- |
| | device | miniature |
| | macroscale | component |
| | tool | convert |
| | microscopic | |

## Revise for IELTS

**Can you remember the test advice in *Achieve IELTS*?**

1 What kind of statement should you make at the beginning of a description of a process?
2 Is it a good idea to rephrase the title of a diagram using your own words?
3 Should each stage of the process be described in detail or briefly?
4 What kind of language and structures should a description of a process contain?

# City life

| In this unit you will practise: | |
|---|---|
| Study skills | speed reading |
| Reading | yes / no / not given; sentence completion |
| Language study | passive sentences; describing changes |
| Listening | matching; multiple-choice questions; summary completion |
| Writing | describing changes in a city |

## Study skills: speed reading

**1** Tick the advice you think will help improve your reading speed.

1 Read titles and headings, and look at any pictures before reading. ☐

2 Speak the words in your mind as you read. ☐

3 Read groups of words rather than single words. ☐

4 Practise with easy texts at first. ☐

5 Set aside 15 minutes a day for reading practice. ☐

6 Don't worry if you can't understand what you read. ☐

7 Time yourself. ☐

8 Test your comprehension – how much can you remember about the text? ☐

9 Use the dictionary – don't guess the meaning. ☐

10 Pay attention to the first and final sentences of a paragraph. ☐

**2** The reading passage is approximately 500 words long. Read it and time yourself, then return to this page and answer the questions without looking at the passage again. Your target is 2 minutes 30 seconds, and at least seven correct answers.

1 Where is Milton Keynes?

2 How is the road system different from other English cities?

3 What does the letter 'H' mean in the names of roads?

4 What was the town of Middleton called before it changed its name?

5 What was first made in Bletchley Park?

6 What happened to Bletchley Park?

7 What is in the town centre?

8 What are *Redways*?

9 What are the lakes used for?

10 Where are the *Art Walks*?

# NEW CITY

**A** Milton Keynes is a purpose-built, high technology city in the south-east of England, 80 km north of London, the capital. Although it is technically a town, it functions as a city with a population of around 200,000 residents. It was designated in 1967, and the
5 original post-modernist design of the architecture was featured in specialist journals and received much praise. Later, however, the original team was disbanded and the buildings became less adventurous. Many outsiders consider it to be a soulless concrete jungle. It is certainly very different from other cities in England,
10 most of which have a radial road system. Milton Keynes' roads were planned on a grid system similar to those in cities in the USA. The roads criss-cross at intervals of approximately 1 km, enclosing 100 grid squares, each of which contains a separate community. The roads have letters and numbers – 'H4' or 'V7',
15 where H is horizontal (east / west) and V is vertical (north / south). It is also famous for its many roundabouts – on one road, the A421, there are 12 in the space of 10 km.

**B** Within the boundaries of Milton Keynes are several historical towns and villages. One of these is the original Milton Keynes
20 village, around which the new city was built. This area still has traditional houses and a thatched pub, and has now reverted to its original name of Middleton. Records of this village date back to the 1700s. Another historical area dating back to the 12th century is Bletchley, where the first computer, named Colossus, was
25 created. Bletchley Park is now a museum, in honour of the work that was done there.

**C** In the town centre there is a huge shopping centre where all the major department stores are represented. The road through the centre is called Midsummer Boulevard, as the sun shines directly
30 along it on Midsummer Day. Along it there are also many amenities such as cinemas, theatres, bowling alleys and Europe's largest indoor ski slope, with real snow. Near the railway station is the National Hockey Stadium, and the city is a major venue for skateboarding, with a 200 km network of paths for pedestrians
35 and cyclists. These paths are called Redways, as they are surfaced with red tarmac. The Redways run alongside the grid roads and have bridges or underpasses where the roads intersect.

**D** Although Milton Keynes is most famous for its built environment and road scheme, it also has some very beautiful parks and woodland. Floodwater from the Great Ouse River
40 has been used to create lakes which the residents use for fishing and water sports. In Campbell Park, which is right in the heart of the city, it is even possible to see sheep grazing at certain times of the year. There are Art Walks in the parks, where visitors can see a variety of sculptures. Taking all of this into account, the people who live in Milton Keynes fiercely defend it as an ideal place to live, despite the fact that it has a poor image in the rest of the country.

# Reading

**1** **Finds words in the reading passage on page 35 for definitions 1 – 10.**

1 a style of building      p _____-m _____

2 without personality or interest      s _____

3 arranged in circles      r _____

4 arranged in squares      g _____ s_____

5 with a roof made of plant material      t _____

6 to go back to an original state      r _____

7 people who walk between places      p _____

8 a kind of road covering      t _____

9 something used to make lakes      f _____

10 a three-dimensional work of art      s _____

**2** **Read the passage again and write ...**

**YES if the statement agrees with the information.**
**NO if the statement contradicts the information.**
**NOT GIVEN if there is no information on this in the passage.**

1 Milton Keynes is not really a city.

2 The road plan was based on an American city.

3 Some of the buildings are better designed than others.

4 Communities are contained between the roads.

5 Middleton is outside Milton Keynes.

6 People in the rest of the UK think Milton Keynes has a good reputation.

**3** **Complete the sentences with no more than three words from the passage.**

1 The shops and amenities are situated along _____ .

2 The Redways are used for walking, cycling and _____ .

3 Redway users can avoid crossing roads by using _____ .

4 Farmers sometimes use _____ for their sheep.

# Language study: passive sentences; describing changes

## Passive sentences

**1** Complete the rules. Use the words in A.

In a passive sentence, the (1) _____ becomes the subject. You don't always have to mention the (2) _____ if it is obvious or unimportant: never end a passive sentence with *by them*. (3) _____ verbs can't be used in a passive sentence because they don't take an (4) _____ . To form the passive, use the verb *to be* and the past (5) _____.

**A** subject
participle
object
intransitive

**2** Make the sentences passive when this is possible.

1 They built Shanghai on the Yangtze Delta.
2 It has become one of the busiest ports in the world.
3 They built a wall around Shanghai in 1544.
4 The population of the city exploded in the 1930s.
5 Many buildings line the Zhong Shan road.
6 The government took away 87% of the local revenue.
7 This has led to rapid industrial and economic expansion.
8 The Chinese are planning 11 new underground railway lines.

## Describing changes

**3** Complete the text with the correct form of the verbs in brackets.

**South Australia and its capital city**

South Australia (1) _____ (declare) a State on 28th December 1836.
The capital city of South Australia (2) _____ (know) as Adelaide, which (3) _____ (name) after the wife of King William IV. Adelaide (4) _____ (design) by Colonel William Light. It (5) _____ (surround) by parkland, and the city (6) _____ (divide) into twelve squares by nine thoroughfares. Adelaide and the surrounding areas (7) _____ (visit) by large numbers of tourists, who come to sample the wine in the Barossa Valley. These vineyards (8) _____ (plant) by German settlers in the 1830s, when they left their homeland because of religious persecution. Future plans for Adelaide include the expansion of the Monarto zoo, where habitats for African and Australian animals (9) _____ (develop) at present, and in a few years' time, a conservation area (10) _____ (add).

Guell Park

la Sagrada Familia

Plaça Reial

Guell Palace

# Listening

IELTS tasks: matching; multiple-choice questions; summary completion

**9** ☐ Listen to a lecture on Barcelona and its architecture, and number the pictures in the order they are mentioned.

**9** ☐ Listen again and circle A – C.

1 Most people in Barcelona speak …
   A one language.
   B two languages.
   C three languages.

2 Avenida Meridiana runs …
   A diagonally across the city.
   B to the edge of the water.
   C around the city.

3 The Carthaginians came from …
   A Rome.
   B Spain.
   C North Africa.

4 The Plaça Reial was built in …
   A 1992.
   B the 19th century.
   C the 13th century.

5 The ground floor of the Plaça Reial is …
   A a concert hall.
   B a shopping arcade.
   C for eating and drinking.

6 The ground floor of Guell Palace is built of …
   A brick.
   B marble.
   C mosaic.

7 Guell Park has …
   A two houses.
   B fifty houses.
   C no houses.

8 The completion date for *la Sagrada Familia* …
   A was 1882.
   B will be 2041.
   C was 2004.

☐ Complete the summary with the words in B.

Barcelona is on the (1) _____ of Spain. The roads in the city are laid out in a (2) _____ pattern, enclosed by a (3) _____ road. Many regard it as the (4) _____ centre of Spain.

There are many fine pieces of (5) _____ in Barcelona. Four examples are: the (6) _____ , a large square surrounded by (7) _____ buildings; the (8) _____ , which even has a staircase for (9) _____ ; (10) _____ , which was designed as a (11) _____ , and (12) _____ , a magnificent (13) _____ which is still not (14) _____ . Three of these examples were designed by (15) _____ .

| **B** | |
| --- | --- |
| two-storey | grid |
| Guell Palace | Gaudi |
| coast | ring |
| la Sagrada Familia | garden city |
| | architecture |
| horses | finished |
| Plaça Reial | Guell Park |
| church | cultural |

# Writing

**1** **Make sentences to describe the early development of Sydney.**

1  40,000 years ago / Australia / inhabit / aborigines
2  1770 Botany Bay / discover / James Cook
3  1822 Sydney / have / banks, markets, roads and police
4  1840 transportation of convicts / end; population / around 30,000
5  1852 Sydney / officially / become / city
6  1848 – 1855 first railway / construct

**2** **Join the sentences using the words and phrases in C.**

**3** **Write the essay.**

> Summarise the information about the more recent development of Sydney by selecting and reporting the main features, and making comparisons where relevant. Write at least 150 words.

**C** when
by
to begin with
not until
between … and
in (×2)

| 1923 – 1932 | Sydney Harbour bridge / constructed |
|---|---|
| 1961 | Sydney Opera House / designed / opened / 1973 |
| 1975 | population / grew 3,000,000 |
| 1993 | Sydney / awarded the right to hold the 2000 Olympics |
| 1996 | construction of Olympic Stadium / started |
| 2000 | Olympic Games / held in Sydney |
| present | 3 universities, 2 museums, population 4,000,000 |
| present – future | Snapper Island and Woolwich docks / redeveloped for commerce and tourism |

# Vocabulary

**🔊 Complete the words and phrases.**

1 Cars must stop when the _ r _ _ f _ _  _ _ g _ _ s are red.
2 A place where roads meet can be called an i _ _ _ r _ _ c _ _ _ n
   or _ u _ c _ _ o _ .
3 A person renting a house or an _ _ _ r _ m _ _ t is a t _ _ a _ _ .
4 Luxury flats may have _ _ e _ _ t _ _ s such as a swimming pool
   or gym.
5 In Manhattan, when you go north it's called u _ _ o _ n and south
   is d _ w _ _ _ w _ .
6 The city of Paris is situated on the _ a _ ks of the River Seine.
7 Barcelona is famous for its post-modernist _ r _ _ _ t e _ _ u _ _ .
8 Shanghai is _ o _ _ t _ d on the east coast of China.
9 The London Eye has become a famous l _ n _ _ a _ _ for people
   in that city.
10 You will need to give at least one month's _ o _ _ c _ if you
   want to leave your rented flat.

# Pronunciation

**10 🔊 Listen to the recording. Between which words do you hear
/w/ or /j/? Write the sound, or No.**

*Examples:* My brother lives in Germany.   <u>*No*</u>
           I owe you a visit.              <u>*/j/, /w/*</u>

1 Go and tell him to come here.      _____
2 Her family come from Boston.       _____
3 Who are you?                       _____
4 Where is the umbrella?             _____
5 I like to visit other cities.      _____
6 He's moved to another town.        _____
7 Los Angeles means 'the angels'.    _____
8 Clear skies over Melbourne.        _____

---

## Revise for IELTS

**Can you remember the test advice in *Achieve IELTS*?**

In the listening test ...

1 what order do the questions appear in?
2 what should you do if you miss an answer?
3 when should you read the questions?

# Language

## Study skills: grammar notebooks

In this unit you will practise:

| | |
|---|---|
| Study skills | grammar notebooks |
| Reading | multiple-choice questions; summary completion |
| Listening | table completion; matching; multiple matching |
| Writing | general training module, task **1** |
| Language study | phrasal verbs; future forms |

**1** You may find it helpful to write down in a notebook which areas of grammar you are learning. Read the different ways you can record grammar in a notebook.

1 Make notes about what you know about the grammar using your own thoughts and personal experience.
2 Write example sentences.
3 Use headings.
4 Make the grammar memorable: use colour, underlining or illustrations.
5 Leave space in your notebook so you can add new ideas later.
6 Use examples from grammar books.
7 Make a note of anything you do not understand.

**2** Read the student's grammar notebook. Which ways has the student used?

Future Continuous

Form
    Will be + present participle
    Will be learning

Meaning
    An action that will be in progress at a particular time in the future

Use
    By 2015, 2 million people will be learning English.
    I hope I'll be studying business administration at University this time next year.
    NB: Future continuous is often used with phrases like 'by'; and 'this time next year'.

Problem!
    Not sure about the difference in use between future continuous and future simple: e.g. Can future continuous describe 'intentions' as well as future activities or events?

**3** Answer the questions.

1 Which methods do you already use to record grammar?
2 Which would you like to try in future?

# Reading

**1** Do the quiz.

## How much do you know about world English?

**Try this quiz and find out.**

**1** Where is *Singlish* spoken?
   A   South Africa
   B   Singapore
   C   India

**2** The word *handy* means mobile phone in …
   A   Malaysia.
   B   Germany.
   C   Taiwan.

**3** Which areas of language may become simplified in future?
   A   question tags
   B   articles
   C   phrasal verbs

**4** How many languages are represented on the Internet?
   A   500
   B   1,000
   C   1,500

**5** What percentage of the Internet is in English?
   A   50%   B   60%   C   70%

**6** If you *google*, you …
   A   want to find information.
   B   write something down.
   C   laugh loudly.

**7** A *cyberskiver* describes someone who …
   A   avoids doing work.
   B   is often absent from work.
   C   tends to arrive at work late.

**8** Which word does not relate to the topic of communication?
   A   blog
   B   zorse
   C   e-lancer

**2** Read the passage and check your answers.

**3** Complete the summary. Use no more than two words from the passage.

One important question facing English is whether it will remain as one language or whether it will evolve into a collection of different (1) _____ . In the past most languages have (2) _____ at some point, just as Latin evolved into languages including French, Spanish and Italian. Present day researchers such as Dr Jennifer Jenkins argue that as English becomes an increasingly global language, we need to reconsider the concept of (3) _____ . She predicts that features such as (4) _____ sounds and words as well as non-standard grammatical forms and (5) _____ will be incorporated into Standard English in future.

# THE FUTURE OF ENGLISH

**A** One of the many predictions about the future of English is that the language as we know it will be spoken only by a minority of English speakers. Other Englishes are being formed all the time. *Singlish* in Singapore is a good example. English was used in Singapore for a hundred and fifty years and when it became independent in
5 1958, Singapore made it the official language of business and government, partly because English united the diverse population of Chinese, Malays and Indians and partly because of its commercial and financial importance. But alongside official English you often hear *Singlish* which continues to grow and develop. Some scholars believe that *Singlish* indicates the way in which future Englishes will
10 develop. In so many ways it fits the traditions of the people of Singapore much better than official English and could threaten to replace it.

**B** Some words clearly come from English, for example, *blur* (confused). But others come from Malay and Hokkien. Words such as *makan* (to eat). Some of these words are now being used as part of Singapore Standard English and they will change it
15 greatly. Marking plurals and past tenses is a matter of choice and so you get phrases like *What happen yesterday?* The verb *to be* can be optional. *She so pretty.* A similar thing is happening in South Africa where local words now sit alongside Standard English, indicating total acceptance and signalling the birth of another new English. Increasingly even in Europe there is an acceptance of different
20 Englishes. Everything does not have to be put in 'correct' English. The Germans use *handy* for a mobile phone and on a Lufthansa flight you will be told to turn your *handies* off. The more English spreads, the more it diversifies, the more it could tend toward fragmentation. Just as Latin, which once ruled over a great linguistic empire, split into French, Italian, Spanish, Portuguese and Romanian, so may the future of
25 English be not as a single language but as a parent of a family of languages.

**C** Noah Webster predicted this 200 years ago. Although he thought it would happen in his native America, the reasons he gave apply to the condition of English around the world today. He wrote, 'New associations of people and new combinations of ideas in arts and science will introduce new words into the American tongue. These
30 causes will produce, in time, a language in North America, as different from the future language of England as the Modern Dutch, Danish and Swedish are from the German, or from one another.' Webster's North America 200 years ago could now be referred to as 'the world today'.

**D** Some researchers believe that the future of English will be shaped by people who
35 speak English as an additional language – those who vastly outnumber the 'core' speakers. Dr Jennifer Jenkins has pointed out that whereas the traditional English *talk about* something or *discuss* something, almost all English as a second language speakers *discuss about* something. She believes that phrases like this are here to stay and will spread into Standard English as, she believes, will the tag *How can I*
40 *say?* and many others. Perhaps even words we consider mispronounced will take their place in the Oxford English Dictionary. In Korea and Taiwan and elsewhere, for instance, a *product* is a *produk*. What odds *produk* will replace *product* as Asian wealth grows? And the complicated English tag system, *have you? haven't you? could you?, couldn't you?* – will most likely be simplified, Professor David Crystal thinks. He thinks that *nesspa* (from the French *n'est ce pas* or *isn't it*) could replace all of them.

**E** 45 The Internet took off in English and although there are now 1,500 languages on the Internet, 70 per cent of it is still in English. And a new form of English has now appeared – *text English*. This is yet another English and totally comprehensible to its users and therefore influential on the future of the language. *I love you* is now more commonly the text, *i luv u*. On Valentine's Day in 2003, in the UK, about 70,000,000 text messages were sent, five times the number of Valentine cards – *i luv u* rules. Here is a word recently accepted by the OED, *blog*, a personal diary type statement placed on the Internet, and
50 the following words may be included in the dictionary in future.

*google:* to search for information on the web, particularly by using the Google search engine; to search the web for information related to a new or potential girlfriend or boyfriend.

*cyberskiver:* a person who surfs the Internet while supposedly being at work.

*e-lancer:* a freelance worker who communicates with clients through a personal computer.

# Listening

P. M. Roget

**IELTS tasks: table completion; matching; multiple matching**

11 ⓪ **Listen to an interview and number the topics in the order you hear them.**

A  Popularity of the Thesaurus today     _____

B  Roget's age when he wrote the Thesaurus   _____

C  Roget's background     _____

D  Roget's interests     _____

E  Why Roget wanted to write the Thesaurus _____ ⚷

② **Match A – D with dates 1 – 4.**

| A  Invention of the crossword | 1 | 1814 |
|---|---|---|
| B  Invention of the slide rule | 2 | 1913 |
| C  Development of the cine camera prototype | 3 | 1852 |
| D  Publication of the first edition of the Thesaurus | 4 | 1824 |

⚷

11 ③ **Listen again and complete the table.**

| **Facts about the Thesaurus** | **Facts about Roget** |
|---|---|
| Number of editions (1) _____ | |
| Copies sold (2) _____ million | |
| The word 'Thesaurus' means (3) _____ | Full name (4) _____ Roget |
| | Nationality (5) _____ |
| | University degree subject (6) _____ |
| | Wrote about feeling and perception in (7) _____ |
| | Invented the travelling (8) _____ |
| | Established a (9) _____ for poor people |
| The invention of the (10) _____ led to an increase in sales of the Thesaurus | |

⚷

# Pronunciation

⓪ **Read the phrases and underline words linked with /r/.**

*the future of English    New Englishes are appearing*
*core speakers    key grammar areas*

12 ② **Listen and check your answers.** ⚷

12 ③ **Listen again and practise.**

# Writing

**1** Read the writing task and underline the key words.

> You have recently completed a short course. The course tutor has asked you for suggestions on how the course can be improved in future.
>
> Write a letter to the course tutor. In your letter ...
> • thank him / her for the course;
> • say what you enjoyed most about it and why;
> • and suggest how the course can be improved.

**2** Decide which aspects of the course the writer mentions.
Read the letter and circle three letters A – F.

A content                     D cost
B length                      E materials used
C number of participants      F location

**3** Put the words in A into groups.

1 thank someone: *warmly*   2 enjoy / like something   3 suggest / think something

> **A** enormously
> immensely
> seriously
> sincerely
> strongly
> warmly

**4** Complete the letter with the words in A.

Dear Rachel Jeffs

I am writing to thank you (1)_____ for the recent Writing Skills course you ran. I attended every session and enjoyed it (2)_____.

I liked the work on dictionary skills (3)_____ and found it particularly useful. I even learned how to use a Thesaurus which has helped me improve my assignment writing. The course has even had a positive effect on my speaking skills as I am now using a wider range of vocabulary in tutorials.

However, you will remember that there were too many students in the class. I would (4)_____ like to suggest that there should be a limit on the number of students per class. Furthermore, as many students intend to apply for summer jobs before the start of the new academic year I (5) _____ think there should be some focus on writing cover letters and CVs too.

I hope you find these suggestions useful. Once again I would like to thank you (6)_____ for such an enjoyable and helpful course.

Best wishes,

Eniko

**5** Write a letter about a different course. Write at least 150 words.

# Language study: phrasal verbs; future forms

## Phrasal verbs

| B | become an adult |
|---|---|
| | become extinct |
| | increase |
| | discover (something) |
| | maintain |
| | recover from |

**1** Match the phrasal verbs with the meanings in B.

1 come across     4 hold on
2 grow up        5 go up
3 get over      6 die out

**2** Complete the sentences using the correct form of the phrasal verbs in 1.

1 Roget _____ in a French community in London.

2 Sales of the Thesaurus _____ after the invention of the crossword puzzle in 1913.

3 Interest in the Thesaurus is unlikely to _____ .

4 The Thesaurus is thematic so you can _____ words you had not thought of before.

5 During his life Roget _____ to the belief that as many people as possible should be happy.

6 Roget established a clinic to care for patients who _____ operations.

## Future forms

**3** Choose the correct verb to complete the sentences. For some sentences, both verbs may be correct.

1 According to figures from the English Speaking Council, in the next ten years, two billion people <u>are going to / will</u> study English.

2 It is predicted that the number of non-native speakers of English <u>will / are about to</u> outnumber native speakers by four to one in the next decade.

3 Next year, all school children in Trinidad <u>are going to / are about to</u> learn Spanish as a second language.

4 The department <u>will / is going to</u> release the results of the English exam next week.

5 Berna's decided she <u>is going to / is about to</u> keep a grammar notebook to improve her grammar.

6 A: Can you answer the phone? I'm busy at the moment.

B: Sorry, I can't. I <u>will / 'm about</u> to go out.

# Vocabulary

Complete the passage. Use the words in C.

**C** words    tongue
varieties    languages
standard    survey
slang    Australian
mate    global
dictionaries

In his latest book, Bill Bryson has written about English, his 'Mother (1) _____ ', and that's the title of the book. Bryson explores the development of English as a (2) _____ language. (He discovers that more people are learning English in China than live in the USA.) And he explains how common (3) _____ like 'shampoo', 'sofa' and others taken from over 50 different (4) _____ came into English. He also looks at definitions of words and how the major (5) _____ were created.

In this fascinating and informative book, Bryson looks at the many (6) _____ of English – from American to (7) _____ , from Creole to the (8) _____ English spoken by newsreaders. And he examines (9) _____ words like (10) '_____' and 'cobber'.

This book is a delightful and amusing (11) _____ of the state of our language.

---

## Revise for IELTS

**Can you remember the test advice in *Achieve IELTS*?**

1 Which four phrases can you use if you need time to think during the speaking test?
2 Should you ask the examiner for their opinion during the discussion phase?
3 Who should do most of the talking during the discussion phase?
4 Will the examiner give a personal opinion about a topic?

# Crime

**In this unit you will practise:**

| | |
|---|---|
| Study skills | collocation (1) |
| Reading | matching paragraphs with summaries; multiple-choice questions |
| Listening | table completion; multiple-choice questions |
| Language study | past perfect; third conditional |
| Writing | general training module, part 2 – addition and concession |

**A**  crime
law
police
parking

**B**  solve    serious
meter    fight
traffic    create
break    and order
violent    criminal
officer    station
ticket    space

# Study skills: collocation (1)

**1** In English many words go together naturally to form collocations, or words that appear together, for example *commit a crime*. When you find a collocation …

1 check with your dictionary and note if the word is a noun, adjective or verb.

2 write it in your vocabulary notebook with the main word.

3 remember it and try to use it in your writing and speaking.

**2** Match words in A with words in B to make collocations.

> *solve a crime    parking meter*

# Reading

> **IELTS tasks: matching paragraphs with summaries; multiple-choice questions**

**1** Read the passage and choose four summaries from 1 – 6. There are two extra summaries.

The fall in crime rates in the USA can be explained in part by …

1 better ways of catching criminals like DNA profiling.

2 not accepting even small criminal acts.

3 the police being more involved in the community.

4 police officers catching criminals quicker.

5 more people being put in jail.

6 society getting older.

**2** Read the passage again and choose A – C.

1 Property crimes …
   A are higher than in Scandinavia.
   B are the lowest since 1980.
   C have fallen by a fifth.

2 Zero tolerance …
   A is the main reason for the fall in crime.
   B moves the focus of police work to minor crimes.
   C is only in New York.

3 Community policing …
   A has three advantages.
   B means the police know the local community better.
   C needs the reorganisation of the police force.
4 As more people are sent to prison …
   A more prisons are built.    B crime is decreasing.    C crime has soared.
5 The murder rate is falling due to …
   A more interesting television programmes.    B easier divorce.    C better protection at home.    ⟁

# The United States' falling crime rate

**A** For the past six years, crime rates have been falling all over America. Violent crime fell by 5% in all, and by slightly more in cities with over 250,000 people. Property crimes have fallen, too, by more than 20%, so that the rates for burglary and car-theft are lower in America than they are in supposedly more law-abiding Britain and Scandinavia. Why this has happened is anyone's guess.
5 The mayor of New York cites his policy of *zero tolerance*: if small crimes lead to bigger crimes, stop the small crimes quickly and the worse crimes will not happen. But is this the main reason why crime has fallen? It seems unlikely. Zero tolerance can be a distraction, making too many policemen spend too much time handing out littering tickets and parking fines while, some streets away, serious crimes are being committed. It is local, too: lower Manhattan may be crime-free while other
10 parts of the city have a high incidence of crime.

**B** New York's ex-police commissioner has a different explanation for the fall in crime. It came about mostly because he reorganised the police department: giving his officers better guns, letting them take more decisions for themselves, and moving them away from desk jobs and out into the streets. The commissioner made his precinct commanders personally responsible for reducing crime on their
15 own beats. In most cities, reorganisation of the police force has been accompanied by an increase in the number of policemen and *community policing*. This means encouraging officers to get out from behind their desks and on to the street. Community policing has two clear advantages. A strong police presence can stop crime, or get officers quickly to a crime scene; and the police themselves get to know their area well enough to prevent crimes, not just pursue the criminals. In some cities,
20 community policing is taken so seriously that it has turned into something like social work. In Boston this includes co-operation between officers and civilians to clean off graffiti, run youth clubs, provide tutoring and counselling services and keep an eye open for truants.

**C** Another possible reason for the fall in crime rates is much simpler. It is a fact that crime rates have dropped as the imprisonment rate has soared. Because more people are being sent to prison, it is
25 claimed, crime rates are falling.

**D** Each of these new changes in law-enforcement has made some difference. Yet it seems probable that the factors that have really brought the crime rates down have little to do with policemen or politicians, and more to do with cycles that are beyond their control. Social trends are also contributing to the decrease in crime. The first of these social cycles is demographic. The fall in the
30 crime rate has coincided with a fall in the number of young men between the ages of 15 and 21 – the peak age for criminal activity in any society, including the USA. Murder rates among Americans have been declining since 1980. There may be more social factors involved: men and women are less likely to murder their partners because divorce is easier today. Social trends also lie behind the fall in property crime. Burglars tend not to steal television sets now because almost everyone has
35 one; at the same time, people stay in watching TV, rather than going out, which deters burglars. Lastly, people are going to greater lengths to protect themselves and their property than they did in the past.

# Listening

**C**
- personal alarm ☐
- security guard ☐
- security barrier ☐ *a*
- security lighting ☐
- keypad lock ☐
- swipe lock ☐
- CCTV ☐

**1** Match the words in C with the pictures.

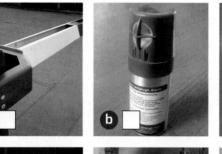
a ☐
b ☐

c ☐

d ☐

e ☐
f ☐

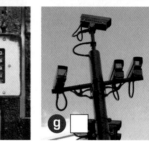
g ☐

**13 2** Listen to a talk and number the pictures in the order you hear them.

**13 3** Listen again and complete the table. Write no more than three words or a number.

## Security measures in halls of residence

| | |
|---|---|
| **security barrier** | people report to guard through (1) _____ before they can enter. |
| **CCTV** | ((2) _____ ) linked directly to (3) _____ . |
| **security lighting** | on from (4) _____ . |
| **keypad lock** | has a (5) _____ security code. |
| **reception desk** | open (6) _____ a day or call (7) _____ . |
| **swipe lock** | opened by (8) _____ card. |
| **windows** | everyone should keep their windows (9) _____ . |
| **personal alarm** | free to all students from the (10) _____ on collection. |
| **university bus** | takes students from (11) _____ every half an hour. |

**4** Tick four things the speaker mentions.

1 CCTV is linked directly to the police station. ☐
2 Film from the CCTV is kept if there is a problem. ☐
3 The guard may not be at reception all the time. ☐
4 Students invite friends into the halls. ☐
5 The security guard frequently finds ground floor windows open. ☐
6 It costs nothing to travel on the university bus. ☐

# Language study: past perfect; third conditional

## Past perfect

**1** Read the articles and match them with the pictures.

a

b

c

**1**

A German man who
(1) _____ earlier in a
local nightclub, was later
mugged again two more times
while waiting for the police.
Reiner Hamer, 27, lost his
wallet containing €120 and
his mobile phone when three
men (2) _____ him in
the toilet of the nightclub. He
(3) _____ the police
from outside the club using a
friend's mobile, but while he
waited three other men came
and (4) _____ his
watch and cigarettes. As he
leaned back against the wall
to recover, another five men
(5) _____ him and
again threatened him, stealing
his jacket and the last of his
money.

**2**

A grandmother knocked out a
burglar by hitting him with a
garden gnome. Police officers
(1) _____ to find the
man still on the roof and half
a dozen people guarding him.
Jean Collop, 69,
(2) _____ up at 5 a.m.
to find a burglar on her roof.
She (3) _____ at the
man, then picked up a gnome
and (4) _____ it at him.
It (5) _____ off his
head, leaving him lying on the
roof.

**3**

A car robber was arrested
after answering a stolen
mobile phone. He
(1) _____ a woman's
car, along with her mobile
phone. The woman
(2) _____ into the local
police station and
(3) _____ the crime.
However, when the police
officer called the woman's
mobile phone number, when
the woman (4) _____ it
ring just a few feet away. The
criminal (5) _____ the
phone while waiting at the
police station to pay a parking
ticket. The woman identified
the phone and the thief was
immediately arrested.

**2** Complete article 1 with the verbs in D,
article 2 with the verbs in E and article
3 with the verbs in F.

| **D** approach | **E** shout | **F** report |
|---|---|---|
| attack | arrive | steal |
| call | bounce | go |
| mug | wake up | answer |
| steal | throw | hear |

# Third conditional sentences

**3** Read the passage and number the pictures.

Police in Virginia Beach charged Charles Robertson, 19, with bank robbery after he made a series of mistakes. He went to Jefferson State Bank on a Wednesday afternoon, filled out a loan application, and left. But then he changed his mind about the loan and decided on a quicker plan – he returned within a couple of hours with a gun, a bag, and a note demanding money. After handing the bank clerk the demand note, the clerk gave him the money and Robertson ran away. Later, realising he had left the note in the bank, Robertson rushed back and took it away. Running back to the getaway car, he discovered that when he had taken back the note he had also left the keys at the bank. Managing to hide from police, Robertson made his way home and told his roommate, whose car he had borrowed, that the car had been stolen. His roommate was very upset and reported to the police that his car had been stolen. Less than twenty minutes later, Officer Mike Koch spotted the car near the bank. The officer took the keys that had been left at the bank. When the officer found that the keys opened the car, he went to the address the car's owner had given and arrested Robertson.

**4** Read the passage again and answer the questions.

1 Why did Charles Robertson change his mind about the loan?
2 Why did he go back to the bank the first time?
3 Why did he leave the car outside the bank?
4 How did the police catch him?

**5** Write the sentences in full.

1 If Charles _had taken_ the loan, he _wouldn't have robbed_ the bank. (take / not rob)

2 He _____ back to the bank if he _____ the note. (not go / not leave)

3 If he _____ back for the note, he _____ the car keys. (not go / not forget)

4 If he _____ from the police, he _____ it back home. (not hide / not make)

5 His roommate _____ the police if Charles _____ the car back. (not call / bring)

6 If Charles's roommate _____ the car stolen, the police _____ the address. (not report / not know)

7 The police _____ to open the car if they _____ the keys. (not be able / not find)

# Writing

**1** **Put the words and phrases in G into groups.**

1 addition    2 concession

**2** **Read the passage and answer the questions.**

1 Who commits white collar crime?

2 How many crimes are referred to?

3 Which ways of stopping white collar crime are given?

| G | additionally | although |
|---|---|---|
| | nevertheless | in addition |
| | furthermore | as well as |
| | nonetheless | however |
| | in spite of | despite |
| | moreover | what is more |
| | yet | |

**3** **Complete the passage with words and phrases for addition.**

## WHITE COLLAR CRIME

White collar crime is generally committed by people with access to a company's money and includes fraud (getting money in a dishonest way), tax-evasion (not paying taxes) and insider-trading (selling and buying shares with special knowledge about the shares). White collar crime usually involves losing a large amount of money and (1) _____ hurts a lot of people. White collar crime damages peoples finances, (2) _____ it damages trust in financial rules and regulations. Tax evasion can have the effect of making government finances weaker, (3) _____ it weakens a country's economy. For this reason punishments for this kind of crime can be severe. For example, people caught insider trading can be fined and (4) _____ they can be sent to jail. (5) _____ governments are trying to stop this kind of crime with better financial rules and regulations.

**4** **Write three sentences and join them with a word or phrase for concession.**

| Some | think | exclusion orders | is/are a good thing. |
|---|---|---|---|
| Many | believe | tagging | is/are a positive development. |
| The majority | have the opinion that | zero tolerance | |
| | | longer jail sentences | |
| Evidence | shows that | community service | is much better. |
| | proves that | meeting the victim | |
| | | counselling | |
| | | education | |

**5** **Write the essay.**

*Some people think that criminals should be locked away from society, but other people think that education is better than imprisonment. What are your opinions on this? Write 250 words about the topic. Give reasons for your answer and include any relevant examples from your own knowledge or experience.*

# Vocabulary

**1** Complete the table.

| crime | person who commits crime |
| --- | --- |
| theft | 1 |
| mugging | 2 |
| vandalism | 3 |
| shoplifting | 4 |
| truancy | 5 |
| burglary | 6 |
| robbery | 7 |
| crime | 8 |

**H** excluded
community
service
tagged
fine
probation

**2** Complete the sentences with the words in H.

1 When she stole another car, Sharon was _____ so that the police always knew where he was.
2 For this crime I am giving you three months' _____ working in the local park.
3 Roberto was _____ from school because he threw a chair at a classmate.
4 Oh no, I've got another parking _____ . That's the third in a month.
5 Lisa went to see her _____ officer every week for six months.

# Pronunciation

**14** **1** Listen and practise the words in activity 1.

## Revise for IELTS

**Can you remember the test advice in *Achieve IELTS*?**

1 What are five stages in answering *true / false / not given* questions?
2 What structure do *problem / solutions* essays have?
3 How many parts do essay titles have? What are they?

# Trade

## Study skills: learning diaries

 Keeping learning diaries will help you practise your writing, remember what you did on your course and help you see how much you have learnt. Read the diaries: which student writes more about their social life and which writes more about their course?

**A**

September

Dear diary,
This is the first time I have ever left Japan. Of course, everything is new and different. From the first week to the third week, my classes were very hard but these were just an introduction. The reason was just I wasn't used to speaking and listening in English. Especially, listening was my main problem at first. It was very difficult to get correct information so I had to concentrate to catch words completely.

October

Dear diary,
I feel some changes in my English nowadays. When I was talking with my Chinese classmates, I realized our conversation was easier than before. Our English still has a lot of problems but I feel comfortable speaking to my classmates even if I can't find a word. Also, I understand why all of our tutors recommend speaking so much. This was the biggest discovery for me. After the day, my motivation became more positive.

November

Dear diary,
I have spent more than two months as an international student. I keep trying to speak English more than before in my classes because my classes are becoming more difficult and I feel these two months have gone very quickly. It means I can't waste my time, therefore speaking in front of my friends and tutors is the easiest way to practise my English. Improving depends on how much I use my classes positively. In addition, the most important part of my life is my friends. Good friends make me feel happy and encourage me. I'm just going to trust my friends and tutors, and do my best.

**B**

September

Dear diary,
It's a long journey here from Taiwan. When I arrived my wife and I spent one whole week to know the neighbouring environment and the location of the University. It is very hard to get used to the accent at first, especially discussing something on the phone, such as getting broadband. Before came, I was like a spoiled child in my family because I didn't know how to cook at all or even wash dishes. Then my wife started to teach me from how to prepare the ingredients and cook 'real' food. During our first weekend, we went to York sightseeing. It was really fantastic and an unforgettable experience.

On registration day, I met Elspeth, the administrator, a lovely woman who gave me a lot of confidence to study here. Then I met most of my tutors and my six fabulous classmates. My classmates consist of three Japanese students, two Chinese students, one Saudi Arabia student and one Taiwanese student (that's me). I won't forget when we celebrated my 30th birthday in a music club especially when all of the audience there stood up to sing Happy Birthday to me — I was so touched about that.

2 Keep a learning diary for yourself.

# Reading

**1** **Read the passage. Do the statements reflect the claims of the writer? Write ...**

**YES if the statement reflects the claims of the writer.**
**NO if the statement contradicts the claims of the writer.**
**NOT GIVEN if it is impossible to say what the writer thinks.**

1  The writer thinks multinational companies are a success for global capitalism.
2  The writer has doubts about the importance of multinational companies.
3  Multinational companies could become less necessary due to globalisation.
4  An explanation for the growth of multinational companies is that fewer people are buying their products in their home country.
5  The writer thinks that multinational companies always move jobs to countries with lower wages.

**2** **Complete the summary. Use no more than three words.**

Multinational companies are neither (1) _____ and are one of the major ways that (2) _____ happens. People associate multinational companies with globalisation, but globalisation could make multinational companies less necessary as (3) _____ and trade barriers fall. There are at least four reasons why companies become multinational. Firstly, they can be more (4) _____ by expanding; secondly, they may buy their (5) _____ or customer; thirdly, they are often (6) _____ , earning high profits; finally, they become multinational because (7) _____ is becoming multinational. However, there are problems with multinationals. Firstly, they can use their power in an (8) _____ ; they can move (9) _____ ; and can use (10) _____ to move profits from high to low tax countries.

# Multinational corporations – the heart of globalisation

**A** Multinational corporations are at the heart of the debate over global economic integration. Their critics say they use their power to exploit workers and natural resources with no regard for the economic well-being of any country or community. Their advocates see multinationals
5 as a triumph for global capitalism, bringing advanced technology to poorer countries and low-cost products to the wealthier ones. Both of these stereotypes have some truth to them. But it would be wrong to see multinational corporations as either good or evil. Companies become multinational in many different ways and for many different reasons.

**B** 10 There is no doubt that multinationals matter. They are one of the main ways through which globalisation takes place. In 1995, the last year for which the United Nations has figures, multinationals had some $7 trillion in sales. Multinationals also play an important role in global investment. The UN's 1997 World Investment Report estimates that 70%
15 of all international payments on technology were between multinational firms and their foreign branches, showing that multinationals play a key role in spreading technology around the globe.

**C** In the public mind, globalisation and multinational corporations are closely related. The stereotype has giant companies shifting production from one country to another in search of the cheapest sources of labour, without regard for the well-being of either the high-wage workers who stand to lose their jobs or the low-paid ones who
20 will be hired. Yet globalisation could just as easily make multinational companies less necessary – as transport costs and trade barriers fall, it becomes easier to serve foreign markets by exporting, rather than establishing factories and research centres around the world. This suggests that the economic logic of the multinational company lies elsewhere.

**D** The most common explanation for multinationals' growth is economies of scale. In certain industries, the
25 argument goes, firms can become more efficient by becoming bigger and producing more. What better way to accomplish this than by serving a global market? Another explanation for the growth in multinational companies is *vertical integration* – when a company buys its supplier or customer. In some industries, the suppliers and users depend on each other and this makes it difficult for such firms to co-operate over long distances. This is the reason many firms integrate vertically and when those suppliers or customers are abroad it turns the firm
30 into a multinational. A third reason for the spread of multinationals is that they tend to be successful. In any business, inefficient firms will eventually go out of business, giving way to those that can earn higher profits. As the world economy becomes more integrated, the companies better at crossing borders are those that grow. There is one other reason for firms to operate as multinationals: because everyone else is doing it. Many companies exist to serve other companies, rather than household consumers. If multinational car manufacturers
35 want to use the same lights in cars which are being built in different countries, then light manufacturers must become multinational, too.

**E** The reasoning above suggests that the growth of multinational companies is without problems, but this is not always the case. For one thing, multinationals' size and scale can make it possible for them to exert power in an exploitative way. A company whose facilities are located in a single country has no alternative but to comply
40 with that country's laws. A multinational, however, can move production: if America's worker safety law is too restrictive, the company can move its factory to Mexico. It can also lower its tax bill by using internal pricing to shift profits from high-tax countries to low-tax ones. This flexibility may make it harder for governments to raise revenue, protect the environment and promote worker safety. Others point out this can be healthy insofar as it forces governments to be careful before imposing costly regulations and taxes. Certainly, many developing
45 countries are eager to be 'exploited' by as many multinationals as possible. Another common criticism is that multinationals are exporting jobs to low-wage countries. Multinationals tend to be motivated more by the other considerations that have been mentioned, rather than by simply cutting wages.

# Language study: information clauses

## Defining relative clauses

**1** **Write the sentences in full.**

1 A place / you can / medicine is called a chemist's.
2 A person / deals with money at a university is / a bursar.
3 The only shop / is open until 11 p.m. / on Richmond Road.
4 *Music Giant* – is / the shop / sells CDs?
5 The new treasurer / someone / is very careful with money.

**2** **Join the two sentences.**

1 Jane took me to see the shop. She worked in it last term.
2 Many companies have been sold. They were owned by the state.
3 The workers are worried about their company. They are employed at Sydney Textiles.
4 The manager was interviewed on television about his large salary. He got a big pay rise.
5 Wei Wei has sold the course books. She bought them last year.

## Non-defining relative clauses

**A**
is 60 today
have been produced since
   the 1960s
died in 1946
I went to University
held against the World
   Trade Organisation

**3** **Write the sentences again including the information in A.**

1 The protest in Seattle was not very peaceful.
2 Sales of Fairtrade products have been rising steadily.
3 The President of the World Bank is in China for talks.
4 John Maynard Keynes was a world famous economist.
5 Adelaide will hold a big trade show this year.

**4** **Look at the information in the charts and write sentences with *most, many, all, some, a number + of ....* Begin like this:**

*Tao, Johnny, Anna, Demet and Carlos are students,*

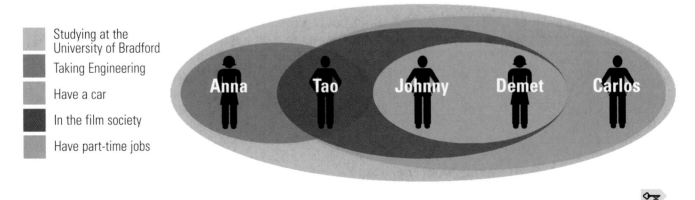

Studying at the University of Bradford

Taking Engineering

Have a car

In the film society

Have part-time jobs

Anna   Tao   Johnny   Demet   Carlos

# Listening

**15** **1** **Listen to a lecture and answer the questions.**

1  How many ways are there of protecting an economy?
2  What is the disagreement between the UK and the USA about?
3  Which country produces cigars?
4  What did France subsidise?
5  Which industry does the European Union want to protect?
6  How many reasons are there for protectionism?
7  What is the overall effect of trade restrictions?

**15** **2** **Listen again and complete the notes.**

> ## Protectionism
>
> Protectionism is the practice of (1) _____ from abroad.
> There are four methods of doing this.
> (a) Tariffs: a (2) _____ on imported goods, making them
> (3) _____ than home-produced goods.
> (b) Embargos, that is a (4) _____ on the import of certain
> goods, but these can result in an (5) _____ economy.
> (c) Subsidies are when a government supports home industries
> with (6) _____ breaks to enable them to compete
> better. This may make producers (7) _____ and
> inefficient.
> (d) The quota system allows a certain (8) _____ to be
> imported, but developing countries think these are
> (9) _____ and against free trade.
>
> Arguments for protectionism
> – to protect (10) _____ in the home country.
> – to stop (11) _____ and save jobs.
> – to protect (12) _____ , especially in developing countries.
> – to (13) _____ for the government.
>
> Arguments against protectionism
> Restrictions on goods affect the (14) _____ so that no
> one benefits.

# Writing

## Formal definitions

**1 Put the sentences in order.**

1  a company / a multinational / which has branches all over the world / can be defined as

2  is / in which the economy slows down and prices drop / a process / deflation

3  is defined as / an accountant / who prepares financial records for a company / someone

## Reasons and results

**2 Read the essay and match it with the title.**

> 1  *Increasing trade globally is the best way of helping developing nations. To what extent do you agree or disagree with this statement?*
>
> 2  *Poor nations are kept poor because of bad deals with richer nations. What are the causes of the problem and what measures can be taken to reduce it?*

When we look at helping developing nations, we immediately think of giving aid through charities or development funds. However, the other side of aid is debt relief. Poor countries are paying $100 million every day to richer countries. (1) _____ of $523 billion given to these countries as loans through the 1960s and 1970s. When interest rates shot up in the 1970s and 1980s (2) _____ because of the way compound interest works. For example, Nigeria borrowed $5 billion, has paid $16 billion to date and still owes $34 billion. To make things worse, these loans often had conditions attached to them (3) _____ to private companies, or leading countries to cut public spending. (4) _____ , people do not have adequate education or medical facilities. Furthermore, some of the original loans were given to these countries when they were governed by dictators, for large-scale projects that did not directly benefit the people or (5) _____ and had to find a lender for it. People in these countries are suffering from paying back debts they did not want in the first place. On account of this, I think that the rich nations of the world should cancel the debt so that poorer countries will have money to spend on public services as well as roads and technology because without this they will not be able to compete in the global economy.

**3 Complete the essay. Use the phrases in B.**

**4 Write 250 words about question 1 in activity 2. Give reasons for your answers and include any relevant examples from your own knowledge or experience.**

**B**  as a consequence of cuts in public spending

this is due to a total external debt

this resulted in many countries owing more than the original amount

causing developing countries to sell state companies

because banks had too much money

# Vocabulary

Complete the crossword.

**Across**

5 This happens when the price of goods increases and the value of money decreases
7 Information in the form of number and figures
9 Money that a government gives a company to keep the price of its products low
10 The money a person gets from his work or investments

**Down**

1 A person who buys shares in a company
2 An amount of money or property
3 A valuable item that can be bought and sold
4 When a person or a group of people has a lot of goods or money
6 Able to continue to use something for a long time
8 A tax that a government charges on products that enter or leave the country

# Pronunciation

**16** Listen and write *defining* or *non-defining relative clause.*

1 _____  2 _____  3 _____  4 _____  5 _____

**16** Listen again and practise.

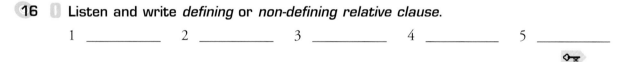

## Revise for IELTS

**Can you remember the test advice in *Achieve IELTS*?**

1 Which phrases will you hear when the lecturer starts a new point?
2 Which phrases will you hear when the lecturer ends a section?
3 Which phrases will you hear when the lecture is coming to the end?

# Opportunity

In this unit you will practise:

| | |
|---|---|
| Study skills | collocation (2) |
| Reading | matching; yes / no / not given |
| Language study | *would* and *used to*; reported speech |
| Listening | multiple-choice questions; summary completion |
| Writing | general training module, task 2; giving examples |

## Study skills: collocation (2)

**1** Match words in A with words in B to make collocations.

| A | | |
|---|---|---|
| career | fire | |
| executive | holding | |
| daily | ethnic | |
| business | internet | |
| flight | police | |
| ten-year | | |

| B | | |
|---|---|---|
| technician | consultant | |
| company | fighter | |
| minority | attendant | |
| officer | contract | |
| opportunity | committee | |
| routine | | |

## Reading

**IELTS tasks: matching; yes / no / not given**

**1** Read the passage and match A – D with descriptions 1 – 4.

| | | | |
|---|---|---|---|
| A | the men | 1 | interested in hygiene |
| B | the hospital | 2 | underfed and cold |
| C | the army | 3 | dirty and uncomfortable |
| D | Florence Nightingale | 4 | not in favour of change |

**2** Read the passage. Do the statements below agree with the information in the reading passage? Write ...

YES if the statement is true according to the passage.
NO if the statement is false according to the passage.
NOT GIVEN if the statement is not given in the passage.

1 Most women in the 1820s only wanted to find a husband.
2 Florence Nightingale had no sisters.
3 Nobody wanted to marry Florence Nightingale.
4 She earned a good salary in Harley Street.
5 Many of the British soldiers were dying from diseases.
6 Florence Nightingale saved lives by making hospitals cleaner.
7 She received financial help from *The Times* newspaper.
8 She used a mathematical diagram to show her results.
9 She believed that women should have to work.

# THE LADY OF THE LAMP

**A** Florence Nightingale was born in 1820, when women used to study only skills which would make them more marriageable, such as music and painting. However, Florence's father treated her more like a boy, as he had no sons. He taught her Greek and Latin, as well as modern foreign languages and mathematics. Although her mother wanted her to marry a rich man, she refused several offers of marriage and announced at the age of 25 that she wanted to become a nurse. Both her parents were totally against the idea. In those days, only lower-class women would work in the nursing profession.

**B** Florence persisted in her ambition, supported by Elizabeth Blackwell, the first woman ever to become a doctor in the United States. Eventually, in 1851, her father allowed her to go to Germany to study nursing. After that, she worked as a superintendent of a women's hospital in Harley Street, London, which was a voluntary position. Two years later, war broke out. Russia had invaded Turkey, and the French and the British went to Turkey to help them against the Russians. This became known as the Crimean War. In those days, people knew nothing about hygiene, and soldiers used to die more often from diseases they caught in the hospitals than wounds they received in the war. 8,000 British soldiers were soon suffering from cholera and malaria in Turkey.

**C** Nurse Nightingale offered to help, but at first she was refused, as women did not usually work in the medical profession. When her cause was published in *The Times* newspaper, she received public support and the government was forced to let her take a group of 38 nurses to the Crimea. When Florence first arrived in Turkey, she was appalled by the conditions she found in the hospitals there. The men would sleep in filthy clothes, and had no blankets or nourishing food to eat.

**E** At first, she met with opposition from the army about her reforms, but she used her contacts at *The Times* to publish reports of the terrible conditions there. Simply by improving the sanitation at the army hospital, she was able to reduce the death rate of the soldiers significantly. She used her mathematical knowledge to prove this, using a statistical device called a 'polar-area diagram', which in fact was the first pie chart.

**E** The romantic image of Florence Nightingale is of 'the lady of the lamp', who used to walk the hospital wards at night, giving comfort to the wounded soldiers. Her knowledge of mathematics is much less well-known.

**F** After the war, she returned to England as a famous and well-respected woman. She met Queen Victoria, and continued her work reforming standards of hygiene in hospitals. She published two books on hospitals and nursing in 1859, and used her influence to raise funds and founded a training school for nurses at St Thomas's hospital in London. She continued to work tirelessly for hospital reform and to support women's rights to have a career, until she became ill in later life. She died in 1910, at the age of 90.

# Language study: *would* and *used to*; reported speech

## *would* and *used to*

**1** Complete the sentences with *would* or *used to*, using *would* when possible.

1 In the 19th century, anaesthetics _____ (not) exist.
2 Very few women _____ work outside the home.
3 When she was a girl, Florence _____ study mathematics with her father.
4 In those days, people _____ (not) know anything about hygiene.
5 The majority of women _____ live with their parents until they got married.
6 Soldiers often _____ have cholera and malaria in the Crimea.
7 Florence _____ want to work as a nurse.   ⟐

**2** Complete the passage, changing the past tense verbs in brackets to *used to*.

Until 1928, women in Britain (1) _____ (couldn't) vote. Most of them (2) _____ (stayed) at home with the children. Working class women (3) _____ (had to) take in washing or needlework to supplement their husbands' salaries, and the least fortunate (4) _____ (worked) in coal mines, where children (5) _____ (were employed) as well. One of the very few rights women (6) _____ (had) was to retain custody of the children if their marriage broke down, but since they (7) _____ (didn't have) the right to divorce without an act of Parliament, this (8) _____ (didn't happen) very often. They (9) _____ (weren't allowed) to study at university, or become doctors. A woman's life today is altogether different from the way things (10) _____ (were) in the 19th century.   ⟐

**3** Write questions for the answers with *used to*.

1 _____ ?
    Yes, she used to work in Australia.
2 _____ ?
    No, I've never lived in China – it was Thailand.
3 _____ ?
    Yes, I used to go to the University of Melbourne.
4 _____ ?
    Well, I sometimes used to visit the library, but now I haven't time.
5 _____ ?
    That's right, I used to own a car, but I had to sell it.   ⟐

# Reported speech

**4 Complete the sentences with the correct form of *say* or *tell*.**

1 The women _____ the President that they wanted equal rights.

2 I never take any notice of what people _____ about me.

3 She _____ him to pack his bags and leave immediately.

4 'I got the job because of my qualifications and experience, not because of my appearance', she _____ the reporters.

5 He _____ that he wished he had been kinder to her.  ⚷

**5 Write the sentences in reported speech.**

1 'This is mine,' she said.                                                     She said _____

2 Hilda said, 'He's going to meet me here tomorrow.'                             Hilda said _____

3 'I'm afraid she left last week,' the landlady told me.                        The landlady told me _____

4 'There is another train to Paris at 10.30 this evening,' Marta said.          Marta said _____

5 'Will you still be here next week?' she asked me.                             She asked me if _____

6 'I'm sure I left it here this morning,' said the secretary.                   The secretary said _____

7 'These rules and regulations are outdated,' said the chairperson.            The chairperson said _____

8 'I resign here and now,' she told him.                                        She told him _____

9 'Can I have another one of these biscuits?' she asked.                        She asked if _____

10 'I'll see you here again next Tuesday,' said Mrs Chan.                       Mrs Chan said _____

⚷

**6 Read conversation A, then complete the sentences in B.**

**A**

**Ali**: Will you read this essay for me, Betty? I'm worried about the spelling.

**Betty**: I can't do it now, Ali. I've just had a phone call from Ivan. He missed the lecture yesterday so I'm taking my notes to his room.

**Ali**: Will you be able to do it this evening?

**Betty**: I was planning to go to the concert tonight, but I'll try to make time.

**Ali**: If you do, I'll wash up every day this week!

**B**

Ali asked Betty if she (1) _____ his essay because he
(2) _____ about the spelling, but she said that she
(3) _____ do it then, because she (4) _____ a call
from Ivan. He (5) _____ the lecture (6) _____ so
she (7) _____ notes to his room.

Ali asked her if (8) _____ to do it (9) _____ .
She replied that she (10) _____ to go to the concert
(11) _____ but that she (12) _____ to make time.
Ali said that if she (13) _____ , _____ wash up
every day (14) _____ .  ⚷

# Listening

**C** self-made
sheltered
advocate
monopolise
aviation
reluctant

**1** **Match the words in C with the definitions.**

1 to control a whole business and not allow competition from other companies
2 not wanting to do something because you are not sure it is the right thing to do
3 connected with flying aeroplanes
4 having become rich or successful without the help of other people
5 protected from bad weather or society
6 someone who publicly and strongly supports something

**17** **2** **Listen to a news broadcast and choose A – D.**

1 Prince Alwaleed is the King's …
   A son.
   B nephew.
   C uncle.
   D brother.
2 Captain Hanadi learned to fly in …
   A Jordan.
   B Saudi Arabia.
   C Mecca.
   D Riyadh.

3 At university, she studied …
   A English language.
   B aviation.
   C instrument rating.
   D English literature.
4 Captain Hanadi thanked her …
   A sisters.
   B flight instructor.
   C father.
   D mother.

**D** employed
in charge
approves
aviator
supported
received
only
astronaut
disapprove
exclusive

**17** **3** **Listen again and complete the summary. Choose the answers from D.**

Captain Hanadi Hindi is Saudi Arabia's first woman
(1) _____ . Prince Alwaleed Bin Talal (2) _____ her to
work for the Kingdom Holding company, which he is
(3) _____ of. She (4) _____ a ten-year contract from
the company. The Prince (5) _____ of women working in all
areas, and Captain Hanadi agrees that women can do jobs which are
usually (6) _____ to men. Her father has (7) _____ her
choice of career, but her mother and some of her friends
(8) _____ of it.

# Writing

IELTS tasks: general training module, task 2; giving examples

**1** Read the question and underline the key words.

*In the past 100 years, the role of women in society has changed. Give some reasons for these changes and say how you feel about them. Include any relevant examples from your own experience.*

**2** Complete the essay with expressions from E.

It is true that, in most parts of the world, women now play a very different role than they did a century ago. (1) _____ is the increased number of women in the workplace, which has risen dramatically. Whereas the role of a female was previously mother and homemaker, women now often work in areas (2) _____ medicine, business management and higher education, which would not have been possible 100 years ago. (3) _____ of the changing role of women is their financial independence. In the past women would have to rely on their husbands to provide money for personal items (4) _____ clothing and cosmetics, but now they are generally able to purchase these things with their own money.

I believe that the main reason for this change is education. More women now study at degree level than ever before, and they are often better students than men, (5) _____ their higher grades and superior study skills. Another reason for women's emancipation is that they have proved they could do traditionally male jobs during World War II, (6) _____ manufacture of weapons, farming and operating heavy machinery, while the men were away at war.

In my opinion, these changes are a positive development. (7) _____ the endless washing, cooking and child-minding which made up the life of a typical woman in the 19th century, one feels fortunate, as a female, to have been born in modern times. It is true that complete equality is still a thing of the future, however, a woman in today's society has more opportunity to fulfil herself than ever before.

**E** if one considers
one illustration of this
such as
another example
like
as can be demonstrated by
for instance

**3** Read the essay title and follow these steps.

*Today there are more women in business and management than ever before, but very few women reach the very top positions. What do you think are the reasons for this?*

1 Underline the key words in the title. (1 minute)
2 Think of your main points and add examples from your own knowledge and experience. (9 minutes)
3 Write the essay. (25 minutes)
4 Read your essay and check for any mistakes. (5 minutes)

# Vocabulary

**1** **Write the job next to the definitions. Avoid referring to gender.**

1 keeps law and order, patrols the streets     *police officer*

2 attends to passengers on aircraft     _____

3 puts out fires     _____

4 controls meetings     _____

5 washes clothes, looks after children, cooks, cleans …     _____ 🔑

**2** **Complete the sentences with the words in F.**

**F**
management styles
interpersonal skills
sabbatical year
human resources
middle-management
performance evaluation
double standards
deep-rooted prejudice
equal opportunities
good-humoured

1 Two examples of different _____ are 'top-down' and 'bottom-up'.

2 The Prime Minister was accused of having _____ when he said educational levels at state schools were excellent but sent his son to a private school.

3 After failing my exams, I decided to take a _____ before I re-started university.

4 Enquiries about salaries should be sent to the _____ department.

5 The police showed that they had a _____ against women officers when they refused to promote Sergeant Wright.

6 Your _____ has shown that you have been wasting too much time on the phone.

7 She's a very _____ person – she never gets upset or angry when things go wrong.

8 The job involves dealing with people, so applicants should have good _____ .

9 The _____ commission is dedicated to women's rights in the workplace.

10 She tried to get to the top, but continued to find herself working in _____ . 🔑

# Pronunciation

**G**
management
performance
educational
applicant
university
resources
commission
prejudice
interpersonal

**1** **Put the words in G in groups.**

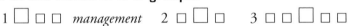

1 ☐☐☐ *management*    2 ☐☐☐    3 ☐☐☐☐☐

**18** **2** **Listen and check your answers.** 🔑

**18** **3** **Listen again and practise.**

## Revise for IELTS

**Can you remember the test advice in *Achieve IELTS*?**

1 What is a good way of preparing notes in speaking test part 2?

2 How long do you have to speak for in speaking test part 2?

3 Why do we use *they* instead of *he* or *she* in writing? 🔑

# Food

## Study skills: studying effectively

**1** Match the headings in A with paragraphs 1 – 6.

**Study skills – studying effectively**

1 _____ Take control. Make a list of all the things you have
to do. Break your workload down into steps. Schedule your time
realistically. Do not miss classes near an exam – you may miss a
review session. Use the hour between classes to review notes.
Plan study time with study breaks. Begin studying early, with an
hour or two per day, and slowly build as the test approaches.

2 _____ Review. Go back over your syllabus, books, and
notes. Identify the most frequent topics, and areas you may have
had difficulty with and start with these.

3 _____ Attack! Get involved with the text as you read. Ask
yourself, *What is important to remember about this section?* Take
notes or underline key concepts. Discuss the topic with others in
your class. Study together to avoid boredom. Read actively,
rather than reading passively and missing important points.

4 _____ Test yourself. Make up questions about key
sections in notes. Often, simply by changing section headings
you can generate many effective questions. For example, a
section called *Causes of crime* might be changed into questions
such as *What is crime?, What are the causes of crime?* and *What are
some examples of crime?*

5 _____ Organise. We can remember information better if
it is organised. There are many techniques that can help you
organise new information, including:
- Write outlines or summaries; show relationships between
  words and phrases.
- Put words and phrases into categories where possible.
- Draw a mind map to organise vocabulary.

6 _____ Place. Recall is better when the location you study
in is similar to the test. The greater the similarity between the
place you study and the test, the greater the chances what you
studied will be recalled during the test.

7 _____ Avoid tiredness. Take short breaks often when
studying. When you take a study break, and just before you go
to sleep at night, don't think about work. It's more important
than ever to take care of yourself before an exam! Eat well, sleep,
and get enough exercise.

**In this unit you will practise:**

| | |
|---|---|
| Study skills | studying effectively |
| Listening | matching; multiple-choice questions |
| Language study | reporting verbs |
| Reading | general training module – true / false / not given; summary completion |
| Writing | repeating and giving alternatives; discursive essay |

**A** I'm bored with books
I don't know where to begin
I think I understand it
I've got so much to study
  … and so little time
There's too much to
  remember
I'm going to stay up all
  night until I understand
  this
I like to study in bed

**2** Decide which things …

1 you do already.  2 you could start to do.

# Listening

IELTS tasks: matching; multiple-choice questions

**19** ❶ Listen to a radio interview and number the pictures in the order they are mentioned.

**19** ❷ Listen again and choose A – C.

1  In 1997, Barry and Sheila's farm produced …
   A  GM foods.   B  organic sheep.   C  sheep and vegetables.

2  Sheila became interested in growing organically because …
   A  she could make more money that way.
   B  it is safer and healthier to eat organic food.
   C  it was a good lifestyle.

3  Before they could start growing organic food, they had to …
   A  sell the tractor.   B  prepare the land.   C  wait three years.

4  In the following year they will expand the farm by adding …
   A  a cow field and barn.   B  50 hectares of land.   C  an orchard.

5  For successful crop rotation, you should plant …
   A  carrots before potatoes.   B  potatoes before parsley.   C  carrots before parsley.

6  Sheila and Barry plan to …
   A  sell wool and vegetables.
   B  start organic sheep-farming.
   C  use the vegetables to pay for meat.

# Language study: reporting verbs

**1  Match the reporting verbs in B with the definitions.**

1  to make clear
2  to have the same opinion
3  to say strongly
4  to put forward as a good idea
5  to say without proof
6  to reach the end of an argument
7  to say more briefly

**B**  suggest
urge
agree
explain
summarise
claim
conclude

**2  Choose the most suitable reporting verb from B for quotations 1 – 6.**

1  'Yes, you're absolutely right. Organic farming is better for the land.'

2  'So, all things considered, I will end my speech by saying that GM crops are the future solution to feeding people in the developing world'.

3  'Why don't you try crop rotation to control the weeds, instead of chemicals?'

4  'Go on, try it. Please. Once you've tasted organically produced beef you'll never buy the supermarket stuff again.'

5  'Well, you see, if you rotate your crops this way, the pests won't be able to stay in the same area the following year.'

6  'GM food is totally safe. We are waiting for the scientists to prove it.'

**3  Write the sentences 1 – 6 in activity 2 again using the reporting verb. The speakers are given below: replace the names with pronouns (*he, she, they*, etc.).**

1  Farmer Barry Watts to the Biological Farmers' Association
*He agreed with them that organic farming was better for the land.*

2  Sir George Bingham addressing the students of the Bingham Agricultural College

3  Mr Ali Khan to his neighbour, Ms Alice Chen

4  Mr John Dunn, the butcher, to his customer Mrs Anne Green

5  Ms Susan Stone to the Shropshire Gardening Society

6  Government representative Mr Howard Hill, on the radio

**4  Correct the mistakes.**

In the meeting yesterday to debate the introduction of GM crops, Gordon Smith urged that the prime minister would commission an independent scientific report. The prime minister insisted to him the report was already under way. Mr Smith then recommended have a second team of scientists to monitor the first group. The prime minister asserted himself to that was not necessary. Mr Smith went on to suggest were the government putting pressure on the commission to produce a favourable report, but the prime minister pointed that this was impossible because the government had no position on whether GM crops should be introduced or not.

# Reading

**1** Read the passage. Do the statements agree with the information in the passage? Write ...

**TRUE** if the information is true according to the passage.
**FALSE** if the information is false according to the passage.
**NOT GIVEN** if the information is not given in the passage.

1 Supermarkets sell more refined carbohydrates than any other product.
2 Low-carb diets are unpopular with the food industry.
3 Shoppers believe that low-fat foods are good for them.
4 Low-carb diets are only effective for the first two weeks.
5 Eating animal fats causes high cholesterol in dieters.
6 Negative theories about low-carb dieters have not been proved.

**2** Read the passage again. Complete the summary. Use no more than three words from the passage for each space.

The (1) _____ is an enormous business enterprise which makes (2) _____ from selling refined carbohydrates in the form of (3) _____ , like cakes and biscuits, to supermarkets. Because of this, the manufacturers do not approve of (4) _____ diets, but prefer (5) _____ diets. A lot of food can be adapted to this purpose by using (6) _____ instead of (7) _____ , to attract shoppers who are worried about (8) _____ , which is believed to cause (9) _____ . Unfortuately, a low-fat (10) _____ diet may be unsuccessful because of the hunger it causes. On the other hand, people on (11) _____ diets eat (12) _____ food, which satisfies them more. Although they eat animal fats, they often have improved (13) _____ as well as lower cholesterol. Some say these diets may cause (14) _____ and that they are only successful because the (15) _____ becomes so restricted, but this has yet to be proved. In general, it is best to choose a diet suitable for the way you live and your (16) _____ . You should try out a (17) _____ if you do not want to fail.

# Low Carbohydrate versus Low-fat Diets

**A**   Take a walk around a supermarket in any developed Western country and you will find many of the shelves are groaning with refined carbohydrates. These include a multitude of starchy snacks, such as potato chips, doughnuts, biscuits, cakes and pastries, which
5   can be produced cheaply and sold in vast quantities. This is the basis of a huge operation which generates millions of dollars a year for the manufacturers, so it is little wonder that the recent popularity of low-carbohydrate diets has generated such criticism and antagonism from certain quarters of the food industry.

**B**   10   Traditionally, low-fat diets have been the norm for slimmers, and this poses less of a threat to supermarket suppliers. Many products can be made with a lower fat content, by substituting lighter oils such as sunflower or olive oil rather than animal fats. By seeking out these low-fat products, shoppers convince themselves that they are making a healthier choice. Concerns about cholesterol – fatty deposits in the bloodstream which may lead to heart disease – also contribute towards this trend. The main disadvantage of a low-fat, calorie-
15   controlled diet is that a restricted intake of food causes hunger, which means that in the long term the diet is unlikely to be maintained. In other words, people can only tolerate being hungry for a limited period of time, after which the diet is often abandoned.

**C**   Alternatively, a diet low in carbohydrates ('carbs') allows you to eat as much as you like, but only of certain foods. In the initial two
20   weeks, only meat, fish, cheese or eggs with salads and fresh leafy vegetables are allowed. To put it another way, bread, pasta, potatoes, starchy fruit such as bananas and rice are all forbidden. Most people lose weight rapidly during this period, and they do not feel hungry because high-protein food is more satisfying. The
25   regime gradually increases the amount of carbohydrates which can be eaten, to stabilise weight loss at the desired level. Initially, some dieters have reported bad breath and other negative side-effects,

but many have continued to follow the plan for years without any health problems – and without regaining weight. Despite the fact that a low-carb diet does nothing to restrict the intake of animal fats, studies have
30   found that levels of cholesterol actually drop, as do blood-sugar levels. In addition, overall health improves as processed foods are excluded from the diet.

**D**   Another concern which has been raised about the low-carb diet is that high protein foods such as red meat may increase the risk of cancer. Advocates of the diet maintain that, as long as enough fresh fruit and vegetables are eaten, there is no danger of this. Opponents also assert that the real reason people lose weight
35   is that the range of food allowed becomes so restricted that the dieter gets bored with eating altogether. As yet, there is not enough evidence to prove or disprove these theories, and the scientists will have to wait until there are enough long-term cases to study.

**E**   On the whole, the diet you choose will depend on your own personal preferences, and your lifestyle. Any diet requires a certain amount of willpower to be successful, and cooking for a family or socialising make it harder
40   to maintain. Although the risks of a low-carb diet may have been exaggerated by the food industry, there is no guarantee that it will be the right one for you. The best advice is to experiment with a range of options, rather than to feel that you have failed if your first choice is the wrong one.

# Writing

**C** in other words
rather than
again
to put it differently
alternatively
to look at it from
another point
of view

**1** **Put the words and expressions in C into two groups.**

1 repeating    2 giving alternative ideas

**2** **Find and underline five similar expressions in the reading passage.**

**3** **Match the first parts 1 – 6 to endings A – H. There are two extra endings.**

1 I only enjoy spicy food. In other words,

2 I prefer to drink water or lemonade with my meal rather than

3 We could go to that new Indian restaurant. Alternatively,

4 I've never had any success with dieting. To put it another way,

5 Fish and meat are good sources of protein. Again,

6 A healthy diet is essential for a healthy body. To look at it from another angle,

A tea or coffee.

B I've given up trying to lose weight.

C I think I should try to eat more fruit.

D I don't like fish and chips or mashed potatoes.

E regular exercise may be equally important.

F there's a very good Chinese restaurant on the High Street.

G soup or salad.

H so are soy beans and nuts.

**4** **Read the question and underline the key words.**

> *Some people believe that making donations of food aid to developing countries does more harm than good.*
>
> *To what extent do you agree with this opinion?*

**5** Choose from A – G to complete the essay.

A  it can encourage a continuation of colonialism
B  it threatens local farmers, who cannot sell their own produce
C  a reaction to a disaster
D  developed countries could be accused of dumping their surplus produce to keep prices high
E  seeds and farming tools
F  food aid saves lives in times of famine
G  in times of drought and famine, they need immediate relief

Every year we hear of some new disaster in Africa or Asia where millions of people's lives are threatened. The West usually responds by making donations to organisations such as the Red Cross or Unicef to buy food for them.

It is true that, if this aid were not provided, millions more people would die. In other words, (1) _____ . People who suffer from extreme poverty have no control over the droughts and floods which bring famine, and they need this help in the short term. Alternatively, it can be argued that, when such aid is given, (2) _____ and therefore may go out of business. To look at it from another angle, (3) _____ .

It is possible that developing nations might benefit more in the long term from donations of (4) _____ rather than food, but again (5) _____ . Many people believe that donations of food maintain dependence on developed countries, or to put it differently, (6) _____ .

In conclusion, it can be said that, although it is understandable that people who have money want to help the poor, this should be seen as a long-term project rather than (7) _____ .

**6** Complete the sentences in your own words.

1  I only enjoy spicy food.
   *In other words, I don't like food that is flavourless / not spicy.*
2  I prefer to drink water with my meal rather than _____ .
3  We could go to the cinema. Alternatively, _____ .
4  I've never had any success with sports. To put it another way, _____ .
5  Fruit and vegetables are essential for our health. To look at it from another angle, _____ .

**7** Write the sentences again. Use the words and phrases in D.

1  A balanced diet prevents illness.
   (healthy) *In other words, a healthy diet helps us to stay well.*
2  Too much alcohol is bad for you.
   (milk, water, tea) _____
3  English food is rather bland.
   (herbs, spices) _____
4  Children eat too many sweets and crisps.
   (apples, carrots) _____
5  Modern families seldom sit at the table together.
   (tray, television) _____

> **D**  in other words
>   to put it differently
>   to look at it from another angle / perspective / point of view

# Vocabulary

**E**  spicy      boiled
   delicious   side dish
   starter     flavourless
   grilled     roast
   sweet       main course
   dessert     savoury

**1** Complete the mind map. Use the words in E.

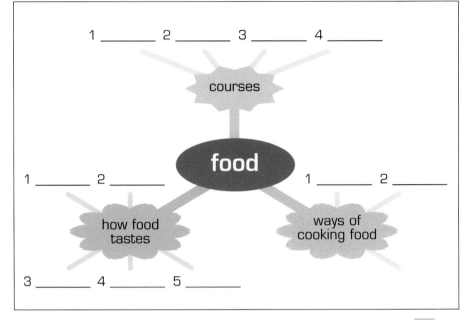

1 _____ 2 _____ 3 _____ 4 _____

courses

**food**

1 _____ 2 _____        1 _____ 2 _____

how food tastes        ways of cooking food

3 _____ 4 _____ 5 _____

**F**  on me
   my treat
   go Dutch
   insist
   get this

**2** Complete the expressions in sentences 1 – 6 with words from F.

1 I know you can't afford to buy me lunch, so let's _____ .
2 Take your hand out of your pocket. I've just cashed my pay cheque, and the drinks are _____ .
3 'Here's $2 for the sandwich.' 'Oh, never mind – it's _____ .'
4 No, no. Please don't offer again. It's my party and I'm paying for it. I _____ .
5 Stand back everybody. I'll _____ .

# Pronunciation

**20** **1** Listen and notice what happens to the final /t/ or /d/ sound.

*one of the first farms     one of the biggest producers     she told me that
and found suppliers of seed     we were on the right track*

**20** **2** Listen again and practise.

## Revise for IELTS

**Can you remember the test advice in *Achieve IELTS*?**

1 What four things can help you understand the views and attitudes of a writer?

# Our earth

## Study skills: learning outside class; study timetables

### Learning outside class

**1** Tick the activities that you could do to learn outside class in your country.

1 Use online self-study programmes. ☐
2 Read English-language newspapers. ☐
3 Watch English-language TV, DVDs or videos. ☐
4 Read books written in English. ☐
5 Form a conversation club with friends. ☐
6 Listen to English-language radio programmes. ☐
7 Find a pen-pal and write e-mails in English. ☐

| In this unit you will practise: | |
|---|---|
| Study skills | learning outside class; study timetables |
| Reading | multiple-choice questions; classification; short answer questions; table completion |
| Language study | phrasal verbs; future continuous and future perfect |
| Listening | multiple-choice questions; classification; short answer questions |
| Writing | cohesion |

### Study timetables

**2** Read José's study timetable and answer the questions.

1 Why has José written in two dates for the test?
2 How long is it between tests?
3 What does José think is his weakest point in English?

| May 20th | week 1 | week 2 | week 3 | week 4 |
|---|---|---|---|---|
| Tuesday | vocabulary revision | timed essay writing task 2, 6 – 8 | timed essay writing task 2, 6 – 8 | timed essay writing task 2, 6 – 8 |
| Wednesday | conversation practice with Miguel and Isabel | conversation practice with Miguel and Isabel | interview practice with Miguel and Isabel | interview practice with Miguel and Isabel |
| Saturday | listen to BBC Worldservice 11 – 11.30 | BBC World service 11 – 11.30, interview practice with Miguel and Isabel | vocabulary revision | IELTS test!* |

*next test:
July 15

**3** Write a study timetable for yourself.

1 Write down the date that you have your test.
2 Decide on the amount of time needed to study for each test section.
3 Remember to allow times for *input* (memorising information) and *output* (practising what you have learnt).
4 Break each session into skills or topics to study and practise.

# Reading

IELTS tasks: multiple-choice questions; classification; short answer questions; table completion

**1 Read the passage and choose A – C.**

1 Dust storms tend to occur in …
   A spring.    B mid-summer.    C autumn.

2 Dust storms …
   A are part of the natural cycle.
   B are from the Sahara desert.
   C have happened only in the last ten years.

3 The *green great wall* is …
   A to protect the desert.
   B 50% complete.
   C being planted in outer Mongolia.

4 The *green great wall* has been criticised because …
   A it uses land needed by farmers.
   B it does not conserve water.
   C trees are being grown where they do not grow naturally.

5 Energy will be provided by …
   A wood.    B sun and wind power.    C waste-water.

**2 Classify the following descriptions under the following projects.**

**GGW Green great wall    GG Grain for Green    CBP Cross Border Project**

**You may use any answer more than once.**

1 _____ was set up in the 1970s.
2 _____ has been criticised.
3 _____ provides finance to farmers who plant trees.
4 _____ is also known by another name.
5 _____ aims to serve as a role model for future initiatives.

**3 Read the passage again and answer the questions.**

1 What three negative effects of dust storms are mentioned?
2 What are the three causes of dust storms in China?
3 What two strategies are being employed to keep dust at ground level?

**4 Complete the table. Use no more than two words from the passage.**

| Type of area | Proposals for area |
|---|---|
| grassland | fence off and re-seed<br>grow (1) _____ for animals |
| mountainous | plant (2) _____ trees<br>develop alternative energy sources to (3) _____<br>promote the development of (4) _____ |
| border | build (5) _____ to support grassland reinstatement<br>irrigate forest with (6) _____ |

# A land turned back from dust

**A** Dust storms occur every year all over China. Between January and May, strong winds blowing to the south-east lift millions of tonnes of fine soil from the plains of inner Mongolia and north-
5 western China. So much soil has been lost that grassland has turned into a dust bowl, while the rest of the dust goes high up in the air to be carried across the world. In Korea and Japan, dust has closed airports and has even found its
10 way across the Pacific to hang as an orange haze over Colorado in the USA.

**B** Dust storms are nothing new in China. In fact, they are part of the global nutrient cycle, in which dust from the Sahara, for example,
15 provides nutrients to the South American rainforest. In a similar way, dust from China improves plankton productivity in the ocean around Hawaii. However, according to Edward Derbyshire of the Gansu Academy of Science,
20 what has happened in the past few decades is that man accelerated a natural process. In China, decades of deforestation, combined with drought and over-exploitation of water resources for agriculture, have turned the land
25 into desert.

**C** In the 1970s, the Chinese government confronted the problem, and began what it claimed to be the biggest ecological project in the world. Under this programme, which has
30 become known as the *green great wall*, trees have been planted to create a barrier that will halt the dust in its tracks. Officially known as the *Three North Shelterbelt Development Programme*, this was designed to protect
35 farmland and aims to cover more than 350,000 square kilometres of land with trees by 2050. It is already almost halfway to its target, converting farmland into forests over huge areas of northern China and inner Mongolia. Locals are
40 encouraged to plant trees which produce fruit and firewood, and farmers are offered cash for planting trees under the *Grain for Green* programme.

**D** Nevertheless, China's reforestation
45 programme has not met with universal approval. There are those both in China and abroad who consider it to be a waste of resources at best, and possibly in danger of doing more harm than good. The Asian Development Bank says,
'Precious groundwater is being pumped to grow 50 trees in the desert, where no tree has grown before. This will cause further desertification and deny farmers the water they need for subsistence crop farming.'

**E** However, planting trees is not the only 55 strategy being used by the Chinese government to control dust storms. Plants and grasses are being planted to fix the soil, and in the northern region of Ningxia, experiments aimed at keeping dust on the ground are under way, using straw 60 mats and chemicals that form a solid crust on the surface of the ground.

**F** In addition to this, China is joined by consultants from Mongolia, Japan and Korea in a cross-border project, set up in 2003. This project 65 team has identified target areas in Mongolia and China with specific types of landscape: mountainous, grassland and border territory. Grassland areas will be re-seeded and fenced off, and crops will be grown to feed livestock that 70 formerly grazed there. In more mountainous regions, Chinese pine trees will be planted. Solar panels and wind turbines will replace burning wood as a source of energy. To compensate for loss of farmland, dairy farming and ecotourism 75 will be introduced. In the cross-border project, a training centre will support efforts to reinstate grasslands, and a forest irrigated with waste-water will provide a model for future efforts.

# Language study: phrasal verbs; future continuous and future perfect

## Phrasal verbs

**1** Read the sentences and decide which phrasal verbs (underlined) are transitive and which are intransitive.

1 People can <u>bring down</u> air pollution by using public transport.
2 *Friends of the Earth* are <u>calling for</u> international action to stop climate change.
3 The Centre for Alternative Technology was established in 1973. A group of volunteers <u>set</u> it <u>up</u>.
4 Energy sources which are pollution free and do not <u>run out</u> are called *renewable energy*. ⚿➤

**A** draw down on
keep up with
make up for
put up with

**2** Complete the sentences. Use the correct form of the multi-word verbs in A.

1 It will be difficult to _____ _____ _____ the damage caused to the global ecoystems by human activity.
2 To avoid _____ _____ _____ the earth's resources, governments need to adopt carbon reduction technologies.
3 It is predicted that we may have to _____ _____ _____ more extreme weather events in future.
4 There is so much research being done on the effects of climate change and global warming that it is difficult to _____ _____ _____ it! ⚿➤

## Future continuous and future perfect

**3** Complete the sentences using the correct form of the verb in brackets.

1 It is thought that we _____ (emit) 400 billion tonnes of greenhouse gases by 2030.
2 It is estimated that sea levels _____ (rise) by between 9 and 88 centimetres by 2100.
3 Over the next century, millions of people _____ (live) in areas at risk of flooding by rising sea levels.
4 Germany currently recycles 75% of its waste glass and _____ (recycle) 85% by 2020.
5 By 2012 the University of Bradford _____ (become) Britain's first *ecoversity*. ⚿➤

# Listening

IELTS tasks: multiple-choice questions; classification; short answer questions

**21** ① **Listen to an interview and choose A – C.**

1 Most greenhouse gas emissions from the home come from …
   A heating and air conditioning.
   B lighting and electrical appliances.
   C heating and lighting.
2 Blue glass can be deposited in … glass banks.
   A transparent   B brown   C green
3 … can be deposited in paper banks.
   A Envelopes   B Books   C Junk mail
4 *Take Back* schemes are operated in …
   A most department stores.
   B some electrical shops.
   C all charity shops.

② **Complete the statements with the words in B. You may use each word more than once.**

1 The *one-tonne challenge* is being run in _____ .
2 Household greenhouse gas emissions are around 11 tonnes in _____ and _____ .
3 Every individual generates six tonnes of greenhouse gas per year in _____ .
4 Electrical appliances and lighting accounts for four tonnes of greenhouse emissions in _____ .
5 Standby power is responsible for 30 million tonnes of greenhouse emissions in _____ .
6 27 tonnes of household waste is thrown away every year in _____ .

**B** Australia
   Britain
   Canada
   the United States

**21** ③ **Listen again and answer the questions. Write no more than three words for each answer.**

1 Which two methods are used to dispose of household waste?
2 Which three items must be removed from glass bottles before recycling?
3 Which two glass items cannot be deposited in glass banks?
4 Which two places will accept unwanted books and magazines and reuse them?
5 Which three items of mobile phone equipment can be recycled in the *Take Back* scheme?

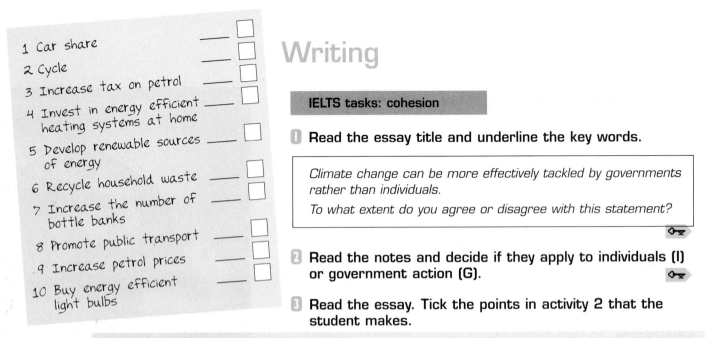

1 Car share ____ ☐
2 Cycle ____ ☐
3 Increase tax on petrol ____ ☐
4 Invest in energy efficient ____ ☐
   heating systems at home
5 Develop renewable sources ____ ☐
   of energy
6 Recycle household waste ____ ☐
7 Increase the number of ____ ☐
   bottle banks
8 Promote public transport ____ ☐
9 Increase petrol prices ____ ☐
10 Buy energy efficient ____ ☐
   light bulbs

# Writing

IELTS tasks: cohesion

**1** **Read the essay title and underline the key words.**

> *Climate change can be more effectively tackled by governments rather than individuals.*
>
> *To what extent do you agree or disagree with this statement?*

**2** **Read the notes and decide if they apply to individuals (I) or government action (G).**

**3** **Read the essay. Tick the points in activity 2 that the student makes.**

Glaciers are melting, sea levels are rising, weather patterns are changing and oceans are warming up. There is absolutely no doubt that climate change is real and it is time to take immediate action to reverse its results.

However, there is a view that climate change is an issue for governments rather than those they
5  represent. After all, they have the power to invest in renewable energy and energy efficiency. For example, they can encourage power companies to switch fuels. They also have the ability to create policies which will reduce levels of carbon dioxide. I think it is true to say that governments could do more to reduce them by developing sustainable transport systems. They need to make public transport more convenient, more frequent and extend it to rural areas. They could also increase the tax on petrol
10  to encourage drivers to use less of it. Part of this money could then be used to fund public transport as well as other, cleaner types of energy like sun, wave and wind power.

However, government action to tackle climate change will not be effective unless individuals also reduce the amount of energy they use. Just as governments try to get private vehicles off the road, individuals also need to use them less for personal journeys. Avoiding unnecessary journeys by car can
15  cut greenhouse gases dramatically. For example, people can avoid using the car for short trips and travel by bike or walk instead. Simple things like these can make a real difference to reversing the effects of climate change. We can take other practical steps to reduce our personal greenhouse gas emissions. For example, Canadians are taking the one-tonne challenge in order to reduce their own $CO_2$ by that amount. This involves car sharing, recycling rubbish and switching to energy-saving light bulbs.
20  In conclusion, climate change is one of the greatest environmental problems of our times and therefore needs to be tackled at both government and individual level before it is too late.

**4** **Find pronouns in the essay that refer to 1 – 8.**

1 climate change (line 3)
2 governments (line 4 and 5)
3 levels of carbon dioxide ($CO_2$) (line 8)
4 public transport (line 9)
5 fuel (line 10)
6 private vehicles (line 14)
7 getting around on foot or cycling (line 16)
8 the *one-tonne challenge* (line 19)

**5** **Write your own answer to the essay title in activity 1. Use the notes in activity 2 to help you. You have 40 minutes.**

# Vocabulary

**1** Complete the passage. Use the words in C.

## OUR CHANGING CLIMATE

### THE PROBLEM

We use (1) _____ for almost everything we do; for heating our homes, cooking our meals and powering our cars. But the major (2) _____ of this energy is largely to blame for the (3) _____ we are now experiencing. When we burn (4) _____ such as oil, natural gas, petrol and (5) _____ for energy, carbon dioxide is released. And along with other (6) _____ , carbon dioxide traps the sun's heat in the atmosphere, leading to (7) _____ and climate change. Over the past 30 years, the number of (8) _____ weather events such as floods, (9) _____ , heatwaves, storms and (10) _____ has trebled worldwide.

### THE SOLUTION

*Friends of the Earth* believes we can meet our energy needs without causing (11) _____ damage to our planet, through investing in (12) _____ energy and energy efficiency. And using the Earth's (13) _____ more efficiently and effectively is good for the future of the planet and the (14) _____ which maintain it.

**C**  climate change
global warming
greenhouse gases
ecosystems
irreversible
energy
droughts
resources
extreme
fossil fuels
renewable
hurricanes
source
diesel

# Pronunciation

**1** Put the words into groups according to the sound of the underlined letters.

c<u>o</u>nservation   fl<u>oo</u>d   gl<u>o</u>bal   p<u>o</u>licy   ec<u>o</u>system   h<u>u</u>rricane
<u>o</u>cean   res<u>ou</u>rce   st<u>o</u>rm   g<u>o</u>vernment   w<u>a</u>rming

1 / əʊ / *so*   2 / ɔː / *more*   3 / ʌ / *but*   4 / ɒ / *job*

**22** **2** Listen and check your answers.

**22** **3** Listen again and practise.

## Revise for IELTS

### Can you remember the test advice in *Achieve IELTS*?

1  How long should you spend on writing task 1 and writing task 2?
2  Can the examiner interrupt you during the speaking test?

In this unit you will practise:

| | |
|---|---|
| Study skills | test preparation |
| Language study | adjectives for people and things; inversion |
| Reading | multiple-choice questions; flow chart completion; table completion |
| Listening | classification; matching; note completion |
| Writing | general training module – proofreading |

## Study skills: test preparation

**1** Put the events in order.

**IELTS test day**

A Leave your mobile phone and bag in the area for coats and bags. _____

B When the invigilator says the test begins, open the test paper and try to answer all the questions. _____

C Go to the test room and show the invigilator your identification. _____

D Transfer your answers the question paper to the answer sheet. _____

E Leave the room when the invigilator announces the end of the test. _____

F Complete the personal details on the front of the question paper and answer paper. _____

**2** Read sentences 1 – 11 and write *true* or *false*.

1 You should arrive before the scheduled starting time. _____

2 If you arrive late, smile at the examiner and sit down quickly. _____

3 You can use correction fluid and highlighters. _____

4 You can give things to, or borrow things from, another candidate during the test. _____

5 If you are not sure what you to do, raise your hand to attract attention. The examiner will come to help you. _____

6 If you do not understand a question, you can ask the examiner to explain it. _____

7 You can leave when you have finished. _____

8 You can put your mobile phone on silent mode and keep it on. _____

9 You should not try to copy the answers from another candidate. _____

10 You cannot use a dictionary during the test. _____

11 It is all right to have a snack in the test. _____

**3** **Tick the things you do during tests.**

1 I read the test paper carefully. ☐
2 I know which kind of questions I answer best. ☐
3 I plan out test time so that I give all the questions enough attention. ☐
4 I structure my answers so that the argument is easy to follow. ☐
5 I answer all the exam questions. ☐
6 I check my answers before handing in the paper. ☐

# Language study: adjectives for people and things; inversion

## Adjectives for people and things

**1** **Complete the sentences. Use the correct form of the words in A.**

1 Doing yoga or listening to music can be very _____ activities.
2 Linguists are people who find studying languages very _____ .
3 Staying up all night cramming for an exam may make you feel _____ the following day.
4 The thought of taking an exam or going for a job interview is so _____ for some people that they have to do relaxation exercises beforehand.
5 I was absolutely _____ when I found out I had passed the exam with distinction.
6 The course was so dull and _____ that I nearly fell asleep. ⊙━

| A | bore |
|---|---|
| | delight |
| | exhaust |
| | interest |
| | petrify |
| | relax |

## Inversion

**2** **Rewrite the sentences.**

1 If I hadn't had my own computer, I wouldn't have been able to work from home.
   Had _____ .
2 Home-working is becoming a common pattern of work nowadays.
   A _____ .
3 The areas of biotechnology, computing and software production have become very important.
   Never before _____ .
4 People nowadays remain in the same job during their working lives.
   Rarely _____ .
5 People without computer skills will find it difficult to find work in future.
   No longer _____ .
6 Most assembly and repetitive work in future will be done by robots.
   Seldom _____ .

⊙━

# Reading

IELTS tasks: multiple-choice questions; flow chart completion; table completion

**1  Read the passage and choose A – C.**

1  The main aim of the article is to …
   A  give advice.    B  make suggestions.    C  describe a process.
2  Who do you need to think about in the decision making process?
   A  your friends    B  your family    C  your competitors
3  Which criterion is not mentioned in the article?
   A  amount of work    B  career development    C  training
4  Who would be most interested in reading this text?
   A  a lecturer    B  a graduate or a student    C  a student counsellor

**2  Using the information contained in the passage, complete the flow chart below. Use no more than three words from the passage for each answer.**

| Step 1 | Step 2 | Step 3 | Step 4 | Step 5 | Step 6 |
|---|---|---|---|---|---|
| Identify (1) _____ members who may be affected by your decision. | (2) _____ what is important to you and decide what you like and dislike. | Put your options into (3) _____ . | Find (4) _____ on your options. | Rank the options. | (5) _____ your choices and scores. |

**3  Complete the table using words from the passage. Use no more than two words.**

| Theme | Criteria |
|---|---|
| Work | pay package<br>(1) _____<br>leave and holidays<br>chances to interact (2) _____<br>travel |
| University | location<br>(3) _____<br>status and reputation<br>(4) _____ |

# DECISION SCIENCE

**As those serious life choices approach, there is a method to help you make decisions ...**

**A**

If you found yourself in a difficult situation with only a few options, what would you do? Would you leave making a decision until the last moment? Would you try to make a decision in the most rational way possible, or would you go with your feelings? Decision science presents a framework to help people think about what they want to do in the future. This might mean thinking about what you want from a job, evaluating job or university offers, or identifying the sorts of jobs or courses you would like to apply for. This article gives you an outline of decision making processes and will help to guide you to the best choice for you.

**B**

When thinking about an important decision it is often difficult to think about all the different aspects at once and to weigh up the relative importance of the different aspects. The idea of decision science is to help people to understand what they want and care about and to structure their decisions and options. The first thing to do is to identify who your decision affects. Your choice may only affect you but if you have a partner, husband, wife, children or you are close to your parents and wider family, your decision will affect them too. It is important to think about who would be affected by your decision and how you can take them into account in your decision.

**C**

The next stage is to structure your decision, to understand what you really care about and what your options are. Understanding what is important to you and what you enjoy or dislike will help you to distinguish between options and identify the sorts of jobs or courses that you might want to apply for. If you are looking for a job, ask yourself these questions.

- In your experience what areas have you enjoyed, found interesting, found challenging or boring?
- Do you enjoy team work or working on your own?
- What do you want to achieve or avoid?
- Do you know what you would like to do in the future, would you like to be in a particular part of the country?
- What is important to you? Some issues people think about are the pay package (salary, bonuses, pensions), workload, holidays and opportunities for social interaction and travel. In terms of a university, you might want to think about where it is located, its size and reputation as well as the course structure it offers.

**D**

You can use the issues that you have identified as important to you to evaluate your options, you might also want to group the issues into themes, if this helps you to think about the options. For example, the issues of salary and pension could fit into an overall theme of *pay package*. Issues of size and location may be grouped together as *organisation*. You then need to put your options into order of preference, in other words you need to rank them. For instance, if you are planning to go to university you need to think about what is important to you and do some research on these. If you decide that the most important things are course fees, reputation, location and accommodation, you will then divide them into sections according to importance. For example, if course fees are the most important factor affecting your choice you will put them first. A student who is looking for a low-cost course (but not the cheapest course), at a university with a good reputation, near their hometown, with accommodation near to the university, may rank their choices like this:

| A course fees | B reputation | C accommodation | D location |
|---|---|---|---|
| 4  low (£3,500) | 4  good | 4  close to university | 4  near home |
| 3  lowest (£3,000) | 3  average | 3  individual flats | 3  overseas |
| 2  average (£4,000) | 2  okay | 2  safe | 2  in a city |
| 1  high (£5,000) | 1  not so good | 1  not expensive | 1  not near a city |

For example, a university with a good reputation for the course you would like to take, which has a good safety record for accommodation, but is not near a city and has high course fees will score like this:
good reputation (4), safe (2), not near a city (1), high course fee (1) = 8

However, a university with an average reputation for the course you would like to take (3), which has accommodation close to the university (4), is located overseas (3) with low course fees (4) will score: 3 + 4 + 3 + 4 = 14.

The university which scores the highest according to your criteria is the one you should choose.

In the next stage you use your preferences and the scores to create a ranking. Then, if there are any uncertainties, you need to think about how they will affect your preferences and see if that changes the decision you make. Finally re-evaluate and review what you did and your scores to make sure you are happy with them – maybe talk them over with a friend if you are unsure. Ask yourself if the decision feels right.

staring — a ②

keeping eye contact — b

drooping your head forward — c

nodding — d

putting your hands on your lap — e

smiling — f

folding your arms — g

tilting your head — h

gesturing with your hands — i

leaning forward slightly — j

# Listening

IELTS tasks: classification; matching; note completion

**❶ Put pictures a – j into groups.**

1  positive body language    2  negative body language

**23 ❷ Listen to a talk about interview technique and number the pictures in the order you hear them mentioned.**

**23 ❸ Listen again and complete the notes. Use no more than three words for each answer.**

Body language in interviews

Body language makes the strongest
(1) _impression_ on people we meet. Making
(2) _eye contact_ often gives a good impression.
During the first few minutes of an interview,
smile to show that you are (3) _relaxed_ .
Nodding shows you are listening and
(4) _paying attention_ . Another good gesture is to
(5) _tilt_ slightly to show you are
listening. The way you carry yourself or your
(6) _posture_ matters even when you are
sitting down. Moving about nervously is called
(7) _fidgeting_ and is a sign that you are
nervous.

Ways to improve body language

Choose a (8) _role model_ (such as a film
star) and imagine you are this person.
Practise reading body language signals by
(9) _watching_ in public places. If you are
being interviewed abroad, find out about
unacceptable (10) _gestures_ . Try to mirror
the interviewer's body language. This is known
as the (11) _similar_ effect.

# Writing

**1** **Read the title and underline the key words.**

> Your college principal has invited you and your classmates to attend an end of course party. He has also asked for suggestions for a suitable present for your course tutor.
>
> You are now writing a letter to the principal.
>
> In your letter:
> - thank him for the invitation
> - suggest a suitable present for your tutor
> - offer to help organise the purchase of the present.

**2** **Read the letter and decide if the sentences are true or false.**

1 The writer accepts the invitation.
2 The writer suggests a photograph as a suitable gift.
3 The writer offers to pay for the gift herself.

---

Dear Dr Jones

Thank you very much for inviting me to the end of course party. I will be delighted to attend. The course has been extremely useful and enjoyed and I have appreciated the help and support of Dr Heavey enormously.

5 I know that Dr Heavey is very interested photography and recently i came across an intresting book of old photographs of Birmingham in a second-hand book shop. The book is in excellent condition and contains some delighted pictures of the college including the main hall and refectery. I am sure that he would enjoy looking them as he knows the

10 places well.

I would be very happy arrange a collection from our group so that we can buy it and present it to him at the party on friday. I can also make sure that all the members of our class sign their names inside the book that will he be able to remember all his students too.

15 Please let me know what you think about my sugestion and thank you once again for your kind invitaton.

Yours sincerely
Lisa Assiz

---

**3** **Read the letter again and find ...**

1 two punctuation errors
2 seven grammatical errors (four missing words, two word class, one word order)
3 four spelling errors.

**4** **Write your own letter suggesting a different present. You should write at least 150 words.**

## Vocabulary

**1** Find words in the square. Words can be read across (→), down (↓) and diagonally (↗↘).

1 Three items of clothing worn at a graduation ceremony
2 Three words which describe negative feelings
3 Three words which describe positive events or situations
4 Three types of celebration party ⊶

| U | S | V | Y | F | A | R | E | W | E | L | L |
|---|---|---|---|---|---|---|---|---|---|---|---|
| B | N | W | K | O | V | E | M | L | B | W | A |
| D | C | I | X | Z | B | G | H | Q | A | N | B |
| E | C | E | N | J | O | Y | A | B | L | E | P |
| L | R | W | X | T | R | B | L | U | L | A | E |
| I | O | Q | U | F | E | F | F | J | C | K | T |
| G | I | U | T | W | D | R | Q | V | M | Z | R |
| H | O | O | D | F | E | E | E | A | C | E | I |
| T | H | G | M | D | P | P | H | S | R | M | F |
| F | C | X | N | W | E | H | C | J | T | R | I |
| U | R | O | B | A | R | B | E | C | U | E | E |
| L | W | R | V | M | I | Y | G | K | T | C | D |

## Pronunciation

**24 1** Listen and count the number of syllables.

| 1 interested | 4 petrifying | 7 boring | 10 ceremony | 13 challenging |
|---|---|---|---|---|
| 2 delightful | 5 enjoyable | 8 graduation | 11 invitation | 14 wound up |
| 3 farewell | 6 barbecue | 9 wonderful | 12 milk round | |

⊶

**24 2** Listen again and underline the syllable which is stressed.

⊶

**24 3** Listen again and practise.

## Revise for IELTS

**Can you remember the test advice in *Achieve IELTS*?**

1 Which three phrases can you use to check your own understanding of a question?
2 Which two phrases can you use if you want the examiner to clarify something?
3 Will you lose marks in the test if you ask for clarification?
4 Will you lose marks for incorrect spelling in the test?
5 Which two types of spelling are acceptable in the test?

⊶

# Answer key

## Unit 1

### Study skills

1
1 English–English
2 on the second syllable
3 countable
4 meaning 1 is about money, meaning 2 is about minerals
5 balance
6 pay / put down / make
7 no – it is transitive and needs an object
8 meaning 1
9 meaning 1

### Language study

1
1 says
2 have
3 Do / come
4 want
5 'm studying
6 're taking
7 'm doing
8 are / enjoying
9 have
10 finishes

2
1 ~~'s thinking~~ thinks
2 ~~'m not understanding~~ don't understand
3 ~~is owning~~ owns
4 ~~'re hearing~~ hear
5 ~~are believing~~ believe

3
1 I didn't catch your last sentence, could you repeat **it**, please?
2 When are you going to start ~~it~~ doing your essay?
3 Bertrand didn't get the attachment to your e-mail. Can you send **it** again?
4 A: Why do you want my lecture notes?
   B: I want **them** because I'd like to read **them** because I was late for that lecture.
5 Okay, is everyone here now? Good, then let's start ~~it~~.

4  1 1B, 2A   2 1A, 2B   3 1B, 2A

5
1 have been waiting
2 have been getting
3 has been solved
4 have left
5 have made
6 have just checked
7 has been rising
8 have predicted
9 has gone up
10 have arrived
11 have been meeting
12 has been waiting
13 have / made
14 have had
15 have been talking

### Listening

1
1 one hour
2 over a hundred
3 introduce new topics
4 main points
5 common words
6 make a note
7 in order
8 a digital recorder
9 smaller classes
10 a short presentation
11 understand different arguments
12 analyse topics critically
13 contribute
14 fifteen to thirty
15 advice and guidance
16 lectures

2
1 independently
2 workshops, group work, practical work
3 after the lecture
4 debate
5 they are not used to this kind of teaching
6 meetings between a tutor and an individual student or small group of stundents

### Pronunciation

1
it's __essential__ to go to lectures
It's __really__ __important__ to go over your lectures
Working independently is __crucial__ at university

### Reading

1  A 7, B 1, C 4, D 2, E 5

2
1 yes (lines 5 – 6)
2 no (lines 15 – 17)
3 not given (the writer does not say whether becoming a representative was easy or difficult)
4 yes (line 27)
5 no (line 34)

3
1 culture, food and background
2 the intellectual atmosphere as she can freely express her own ideas
3 the decision to cancel a module
4 teaches children and helps the elderly
5 extra-curricular activities

### Vocabulary

1 finance
1 eligible     3 applicant
2 fund         4 grant

good characteristics
1 independent
2 intelligent
3 organised
4 enthusiastic
5 bright
6 hardworking

bad characteristics
1 lazy
2 spoilt

### Writing

1
1 The number of students from the United States studying in Europe
2 The number of US students going to the Middle East is falling; the number of students going to South America, Africa and Australasia is rising; the number going to Asia and Canada is stable.
3 a false
  b false – it rose significantly
  c false – it dropped dramatically

2
1 bar charts
2 between 1985 and 2004
3 In general
4 long term trend
5 declined
6 climbed
7 very dramatic rise
8 remained quite constant
9 overall number

### Revise for IELTS

1 The title, charts, tables, pictures, names and numbers.

2 It helps you use your knowledge and experience to understand the passage.

## Unit 2

### Study skills

1
1 dear        4 locate
2 put in      5 in charge
3 capability

2
6 inexpensive   9 misplace
7 uninstall    10 irresponsible
8 inability

# Listening

**1** course fees ✓
management, marketing
full-time ✓
postgraduate ✓
MA ✓
PMKTMAN
direct debit ✓
Per Jensen
UB606 133

**2**  1  On his letter of acceptance
2  £10,250
3  If he is ill
4  The sort code and account number (and receipt)

# Reading

**1**  1 CM, 2 RM, 3 FM,
4 RM, 5 FM, 6 CM

**2**  1  false (lines 8 – 9)
2  true (line 15)
3  true (line 24)
4  true (lines 30 – 31)
5  not given (in lines 34 – 35 the writer says that gold has a very small role, silver may also have a very small role, but this is not stated in the passage)
6  false (lines 44 – 45)

# Language study

**1**  1  How do you spell *commerce*?
2  What's the meaning of *makan* in English?
3  How do you pronounce *debt*?
4  Can you tell me what *disticaret* means in English?
5  Could you repeat that, please?
6  What does *paying-in book* mean?
7  What's the opposite of *well-off*?
8  Is there another word for *dollar*?

**2**  1 c, 2 e, 3 g, 4 d, 5 a, 6 h, 7 b, 8 f

**3**  1  Which bank did you open an account with?
2  How much is it / does it cost to send money overseas (electronically)?
3  Could you tell me where the nearest cash point is?
4  Have you got change for £1?
5  What is the exchange rate for rupees to pounds?

**4**  1  anti-government  4  problem-free
2  unbelievable  5  improbable
3  inexpensive  6  penniless

# Writing

**1**  1  £100
2  It has already charged the student £25. It might charge the student another £25.

**2**  Dear Mr Appleby
Please accept my apologies for exceeding

---

my overdraft limit. I went over my overdraft limit of £100 on Friday evening as I had to pay for a taxi from the city centre back to the campus as this is much safer than walking home alone.

However, I paid back the amount on Monday as soon as the bank was open in the hope that I would not be charged for exceeding my overdraft limit. I was very disappointed to find that I had been charged £25 when I received your letter yesterday.

As the amount was paid back immediately I would be very grateful if you would take back the charge of £25.

With thanks
Ms Norma Bates

**3**  You had to pay your university course fees last week. Unfortunately you are still waiting for money to arrive in your new bank account from your home country. The university has written to you asking for immediate payment, saying they have charged you extra because of the delay.

Write a letter to the university. Explain what has happened and tell them what you want to do about it.

**4**  Suggested answer
Dear Sir or Madam
I am writing to explain the delay in paying my university course fees which should have been paid last week. The delay in payment has been caused because of the slow transfer of money from my bank in my home country to this country. I do not know whether this delay has been caused by banks in this country or in my country. However, when my family asked the bank branch in my town to find the reason for the delay, the bank said that they had sent the amount last month. For this reason I am trying to find where the amount was sent, but this may take some time.

As this delay is beyond my control and I have been doing everything possible to find where the amount has been sent, I hope that the university will be able to take back the fine. Furthermore, I hope that the university will be able to wait for payment until I have resolved the situation.

Yours sincerely

**5**  1  They need money for basic essentials.
2  To have a nice place to live.
3  They could save money by not going out.
4  43% think work affects their studies.

**6**  1  majority  2  over  3  almost
4  third  5  minority

**7**  Suggested answer
The three charts show the reasons why

---

students work, how students could save money and what percentage of students thought that working affected their studies adversely.

Overall, we can see that the majority of students, at nearly 70%, work because they need to earn money for everyday necessities. Just over 40% of students use the money from working in order to go out and about a third of students work in order to buy new clothes and around 15% work to live in nice accommodation.

At the same time, the majority of students think they could save money by going out less frequently. Over 40% said they could save money by buying fewer clothes and just under 40% say they could spend less on their mobile phones. A similar percentage worked to earn money for going out. Just under 40% feel that working would give them extra skills, and around 12% needed the money to pay their course fees. Only one fifth of the students felt that they could save money on accommodation.

The pie chart shows that students who feel their studies are not affected by working at the same time are in the minority – just over one third of students disagreed with the statement. However, 43% agreed that employment has a negative effect. At the same time, 18% had no opinion on this.

# Vocabulary

**1**  1  charge  6  overdraft
2  withdraw  7  debit card
3  deposit  8  cash point
4  quarter  9  sort code
5  account  10  bankrupt
**Missing word:** cheque book

# Pronunciation

**1**  1  bankrupt, transfer, statement, balance, purchase, payment
2  account, exchange, convert, withdraw

# Revise for IELTS

**1**  The answer may be the opposite or the negative of words in the question.
2  Organising and describing the information.
3  You have a limited amount of time so writing about something you will not receive points for is wasting time.

---

# Unit 3

## Study skills

1 i, 2 e, 3 a, 4 g, 5 b,
6 j, 7 c, 8 f, 9 d, 10 h

## Reading

1 N (line 2), 2 N (line 5),
3 N (lines 8–10), 4 N (line 17), 5 NG,
6 Y (line 22), 7 NG, 8 Y (line 23),
9 Y (line 29), 10 Y (line 31)

## Listening

1  a   chairlift        e   underground train
   b   steam train      f   diesel train
   c   trolley-bus      g   tram
   d   bus              h   funicular train

2  1 g, 2 d, 3 c, 4 e, 5 f, 6 h, 7 a, 8 b

3  1 C, 2 B, 3 A, 4 B, 5 D, 6 C

## Language study

1  1  highest
   2  tallest
   3  taller
   4  highest
   5  widest

2  1  is not as small as Prague
   2  is as beautiful as Vietnam
   3  was as hot as Dubai today
   4  is not as far from Singapore as
      Tasmania
   5  is as pleasant to fly with as British
      Airways

3  1  boring, expensive, mountainous,
      exotic, pointed, powerful, efficient,
      difficult, economical, enjoyable
   2  hot, near, fast, long, cool, great,
      heavy, slight, light, noisy
   3  far, good, bad

4  **Possible answers**
   2  A tram is somewhat slower than a
      bus.
      A bus is a little bit more comfortable
      than a tram.
   3  A Maglev is a great deal faster than a
      steam train.
      A steam train is considerably noisier
      than a Maglev.
   4  A Shinkansen is a little bit noisier
      than a Maglev.
      A Maglev is somewhat faster than a
      Shinkansen.

5  1  put / accelerated
   2  invested / began
   3  took
   4  bought / went
   5  cost / flew

6  1  was shining        6  arrived
   2  decided            7  was pouring
   3  wasn't raining     8  got
   4  didn't take        9  didn't leave
   5  left              10  didn't want

   11  were doing        18  was standing
   12  heard             19  ran
   13  groaned           20  invited
   14  stopped           21  had
   15  came              22  were running
   16  didn't know       23  got
   17  saw

7  2  didn't you take your
   3  did you arrive
   4  didn't you leave
   5  were the / doing
   6  was / standing
   7  Were the trains running
   8  Did you have / Were there

## Writing

1  1  in comparison with, in the same
      way, compared with, at the same
      time, the same as
   2  conversely, on the other hand, in
      contrast to this, on the contrary, by
      contrast

2  1 36%, 2 20%, 3 8%

3  1 any from group 2; 2 the same as;
   3 conversely / in contrast to this / on
   the other hand / by contrast; 4 in the
   same way / at the same time;
   5 conversely / on the other hand / in
   contrast to this / by contrast; 6 any
   from group 2; 7 compared with / in
   comparison with; 8 on the other hand /
   in contrast to this / by contrast

4  **Suggested answer**
The first table shows the reasons why
some people in the UK prefer to cycle
to work. Conversely, the second table
gives reasons for those who choose to go
to work by car.
The highest percentage of those who
favour cycling say that this is because
riding a bicycle to work is healthier than
driving. 30% of them gave this as a
reason. The same amount of people,
30% say that they cycle to work because
it causes less pollution. 13% of people
cycle to work because it is cheaper than
driving. Surprisingly, a similar amount
of people said that they cycled to work
because it is faster than travelling by car.
In contrast to this, the percentage who
prefer to travel by car because it is more
comfortable is 40%. The two least
important reasons for going to work by
car, with 14% and 11% respectively, is
that people need to carry things to work
and that it is safer than cycling to work.
Finally, 16% say they prefer driving
because it is faster than cycling. This
contrasts with the cyclists who ride to
work because it is faster than driving.
In general, it seems that the majority of
people who cycle to work do this for
health and  environmental reasons. By
contrast, those who travel by car want
to have a more comfortable journey
over longer distances.

## Vocabulary

1  Air travel: cockpit, hold, fuselage, gate,
   lounge, check-in, tail fin, wingspan,
   galley, steward, pilot, boarding card
   Rail Travel: track, railcard, carriage,
   platform, barrier, signals, guard, driver,
   waiting room

2  1  wingspan         7  fuselage
   2  lounge           8  check-in,
   3  barrier             boarding card,
   4  cockpit             steward
   5  railcard         9  track
   6  carriages       10  platform

## Pronunciation

1  1  dropped, missed, picked, wished,
      worked, produced
   2  travelled, climbed, arrived, sailed,
      carried, performed, entered, listened
   3  invited, boarded, mended, recorded,
      invested, tested

2  1  / d /        2 / t /        3 / ɪd /

## Revise for IELTS

1  When you correct yourself if you
   make a mistake.
2  Contrasting each reason in order of
   importance or contrasting all the
   information in one table with all the
   information in the second.

# Unit 4

## Study skills

1  1  post-it notes     4  notebook
   2  file card         5  laptop
   3  personal organiser

2  1  A notebook, laptop
      B file card, post-it notes
      C laptop, personal organiser
      D laptop, notebook, file card
   2  A note book, laptop
      B file cards
      C personal organiser
   3  You should put as much
      information as possible.
4–6  Open answers

## Reading

1  a   Robot V          d   Entomopter
   b   Scorpion         e   Spirit
   c   Whegs 2™

2  1 B, 2 A, 3 C, 4 C, 5 B

3  1 E, 2 O, 3 S, 4 S, 5 O, 6 W, 7 R,
   8 O, 9 S, 10 R, 11 W, 12 R, 13 O

## Listening

**1** 1 L, 2 P, 3 H, 4 P, 5 H, 6 L

**2**
| | | | |
|---|---|---|---|
| 1 | theatre | 6 | depth |
| 2 | downloading | 7 | taking place |
| 3 | control | 8 | image |
| 4 | video games | 9 | side and back |
| 5 | flat | 10 | wireless |

## Pronunciation

**1** here to <u>tell us</u> more
you <u>can even</u> walk <u>part of</u> the way
when we <u>talk about</u> dimensions

## Language study

**1**
1 are called
2 are sent / experience
3 is being developed
4 are shown
5 developed / is designed
6 grows

**2**
1 Songs are being released directly to the consumer.
2 31 million hours of new TV shows are produced each year.
3 Projection screens can be placed throughout the house.
4 A television company developed a digital storytelling project last year.
5 Children are encouraged to make their own documentaries online.

**3**
2 Who was the World Wide Web invented by?
3 Who is given more control and choice (by new technology)?
4 What is being made slimmer and lighter?
5 Who is giving us more choice of programmes?

## Writing

**1**
1 contains two gases
2 turning it on
3 it begins to glow
4 a 100% reflective mirror goes at the other
5 forth between the two mirrors
6 the fully reflective mirror makes all of the light bounce off it

**2** Lasers are very simple tools, especially the lasers which <u>are used</u> to make most holograms. A laser <u>is made</u> up of a very thin glass tube, about the size of a drinking straw and contains two gases – helium and neon. The laser <u>is called</u> a helium-neon laser. <u>The first stage</u> of the process involves plugging the laser into the wall and turning it on. <u>Following this</u>, electricity passes through this gas and it begins to glow. <u>In order to</u> get the laser beam out of this tube, two mirrors <u>are placed</u> at both ends of the tube: one partially reflective mirror <u>is placed</u> at one end and a 100% reflective mirror

goes at the other. The result is that light begins to bounce back and forth between the two mirrors. The partially reflective mirror lets some of the light pass through and the fully reflective mirror makes all of the light bounce off it. <u>Finally</u>, the light that passes through comes out as the laser beam.

**3** The diagram shows how a <u>3D television system</u> works. <u>Summarise the information</u> by selecting and reporting the <u>main features</u> and <u>making comparisons</u> where relevant. You should write <u>at least 150 words</u>.

**4**
| | | | |
|---|---|---|---|
| 1 | is constituted of | 4 | subsequently |
| 2 | The first step | 5 | so that |
| 3 | Next | 6 | Eventually |

**5**
1 The diagram shows a television system which can display 3-D pictures to people sitting in different parts of a room.
2 The system is constituted of cameras, a screen and a filter.
3 line 5 – end
4 Following this / in order to / then / subsequently / the first step / eventually / next / so that
5 are generated / are displayed / is fitted / is created

**6 Suggested answer**
A podcast is a sound recording which is put on to the Internet so that other people can download it and listen to it. In order to make a podcast, you need four items. These are a microphone, a computer, a sound recording program, and an Internet connection. To listen to a podcast you need an Internet connection, a computer and an MP3 player. There are four steps in the process of podcasting. Firstly, the microphone is connected to the computer and then your programme is recorded via a sound recording program. Having done this, the computer is connected to the Internet and then the sound file is uploaded to a podcasting website that anyone can access. In order to listen to the programme, the other person has to connect their computer to the podcast website through the Internet. Following this, the sound file is downloaded to the listener's computer and the sound file is eventually transferred to an MP3 player so the listener can hear the programme wherever they go.

## Vocabulary

**1**
1 device, component, tool
2 crystallise, adapt, convert
3 macroscale, microscopic, miniature

## Revise for IELTS

1 A general description.

2 Yes.
3 Briefly.
4 Passive structures, phrases of purpose and phrases for staging and sequencing.

# Unit 5
## Study skills

**1**
1 Yes: these will help you to predict the content of the passage before you read, and will give you a general idea of the topic.
2 No: this technique is known as 'vocalisation' and will slow you down. You can read faster than you can speak.
3 Yes: you should be able to read at least three words at a time, so that your eyes need to make fewer movements. Your eyes can read ahead of your brain.
4 Yes: you cannot improve reading speed on difficult texts. Choose something you enjoy reading, with not more than six to seven words per page that you do not understand.
5 Yes: get into the habit of reading whenever you can. Keep a book or magazine in your bag to read on public transport, or while you are eating.
6 No: there is no point in reading fast if you have no comprehension.
7 Yes: use a text of a known length, or work out the approximate number of words on a page (count the words in one line, then the number of lines on the page). You should be able to read at least 500 words in 2 minutes – a reading speed of 250 wpm. You can buy special books to practise this.
8 Yes: stop after you have read a passage and summarise it in your mind.
9 No: dictionaries slow you down. You should develop the skill of using the context (surrounding words) to guess the meaning. You probably already do this in your own language.
10 Yes: most topic sentences occur in the first place, less often they are in the final position. The topic sentence summarises the main point of the paragraph.

**2**
1 south-east England / 80 km from London (line 2)
2 it is built on a grid system / like the USA (lines 10–12)
3 horizontal (line 15)
4 Milton Keynes village (lines 20—22)

5 a computer (lines 24–25)
6 It became a museum. (line 25)
7 a shopping centre (line 27)
8 paths for pedestrians and cyclists (line 35)
9 fishing and watersports (line 40)
10 in the parks (lines 41–42)

# Reading

**1**
1 post-modernist    6 revert
2 soulless    7 pedestrians
3 radial    8 tarmac
4 grid system    9 floodwater
5 thatched    10 sculpture

**2** 1 Y (line 3), 2 NG, 3 Y (lines 6 – 8),
4 Y (lines 12 – 13), 5 N (line 18),
6 N (lines 43 – 44)

**3**
1 Midsummer Boulevard
2 skateboarding
3 bridges or underpasses
4 Campbell Park

# Language study

**1**
1 object    4 object
2 subject    5 participle
3 intransitive

**2**
1 Shanghai was built on the Yangtze Delta.
2 Not possible
3 A wall was built around Shanghai in 1544.
4 Not possible
5 The Zhong Shan road is lined with many buildings.
6 87% of the local revenue was taken away by the government.
7 Not possible
8 11 new underground railways are being planned (by the Chinese).

**3**
1 was declared
2 is known
3 was named
4 was designed
5 is surrounded
6 is divided
7 are visited
8 were planted
9 are being developed
10 will be added

# Listening

**1** 3, 4, 1, 2
**2** 1 B, 2 A, 3 C, 4 B, 5 C, 6 A, 7 A, 8 B
**3**
1 coast    9 horses
2 grid    10 Guell Park
3 ring    11 garden city
4 cultural    12 la Sagrada
5 architecture      Familia
6 Plaça Reial    13 church
7 two-storey    14 finished
8 Guell Palace    15 Gaudi

# Writing

**1 and 2 Suggested answer**
To begin with, 40,000 years ago Australia was inhabited by aborigines. In 1770 Botany Bay was discovered by James Cook. By 1882 Sydney had banks, markets, roads and police. When the transportation of convicts was ended in 1840 the population was around 30,000. It was not until 1852, however, that Sydney officially became a city. Between 1848 and 1855 the first railway was constructed.

**3 Suggested answer**
Between 1923 and 1932 Sydney Harbour Bridge was constructed. In 1961 Sydney Opera House was designed and was opened in 1973. By 1975 the population had grown to 3,000,000. In 1993 Sydney was awarded the right to hold the 2000 Olympics and construction of the Olympic Stadium was started in 1996. In 2000 the Olympic games were held in Sydney. Today, Sydney has three universities and a population of 4,000,000. In the future, Snapper Island and Woolwich docks, situated to the north of the city centre, will be redeveloped for commercial and tourist use.

# Vocabulary

**1**
1 traffic lights
2 intersection / junction
3 apartment / tenant
4 amenities
5 uptown / downtown
6 banks
7 architecture
8 located
9 landmark
10 notice

# Pronunciation

**1** 1 /w/   2 no   3 /w/   4 /j/
5 no   6 /w/   7 /j/   8 no

# Revise for IELTS

1 In the same order as they occur in the passage.
2 Move on to the next question.
3 Before the listening passage begins.

# Unit 6
## Study skills

**2** 1, 2, 3, 4, 6, 7

# Reading

**2** 1 B, 2 B, 3 A, 4 C, 5 C, 6 A, 7 A, 8 B
**3**
1 Englishes
2 split
3 standard /correct English
4 mispronounced
5 phrases

# Listening

**1** A 5, B 3, C 1, D 2, E 4
**2** A 2, B 1, C 4, D 3
**3**
1 150    7 animals
2 32    8 chess set
3 treasure house    9 clinic
4 Peter Mark    10 crossword puzzle
5 French
6 Medicine

# Pronunciation

**1** the fut<u>ure of</u> English
New Englishes <u>are appearing</u>
core speakers (no linking)
key gramma<u>r areas</u>

# Writing

**1** thank, say what you enjoyed, suggest
**2** A, C, E
**3**
1 warmly, sincerely
2 immensely, enormously
3 seriously, strongly
**4**
1 sincerely/warmly
2 immensely/ enormously
3 immensely/ enormously
4 strongly/seriously
5 seriously
6 sincerely/warmly

# Language study

**1**
1 come across    discover (something)
2 grow up    become an adult
3 get over    recover from
4 hold on    maintain
5 go up    increase
6 die out    become extinct
**2**
1 grew up    4 come across
2 went up    5 held on
3 die out    6 were getting over
**3**
1 both 2 will      3 are going to
4 both 5 is going to 6 'm about to

# Vocabulary

**1**
1 tongue    7 Australian
2 global    8 standard
3 words    9 slang
4 languages    10 mate
5 dictionaries    11 survey
6 varieties

## Revise for IELTS

1 just a (second), let me (think), give me a (moment), that's a good question
2 No
3 The candidate
4 No

# Unit 7
## Study skills

2 
| | |
|---|---|
| traffic police | fight crime |
| break a law | create a law |
| violent crime | law and order |
| police officer | criminal law |
| parking ticket | police station |
| serious crime | parking space |

## Reading

1 A 2, B 3, C 5, D 6
2 1 C, 2 B, 3 B, 4 B, 5 B

## Listening

1 
| | | | |
|---|---|---|---|
| a | security barrier | e | swipe lock |
| b | personal alarm | f | keypad lock |
| c | security lighting | g | CCTV |
| d | security guard | | |

2 
| | | | |
|---|---|---|---|
| 1 | security barrier | 5 | security guard |
| 2 | CCTV | 6 | swipe lock |
| 3 | security lighting | 7 | personal alarm |
| 4 | keypad lock | | |

3 
1 the speaker
2 closed circuit television
3 the security office
4 night to morning
5 four digit
6 24-hours
7 9666
8 student
9 locked
10 Students' Union
11 campus to town

4 2, 3, 5, 6

## Language study

1 1 b, 2 a, 3 c
2 
| | | | |
|---|---|---|---|
| 1 | had been mugged | 3 | called |
| | | 4 | stole |
| 2 | attacked | 5 | approached |

| | | | |
|---|---|---|---|
| 1 | arrived | 4 | (had) thrown |
| 2 | (had woken up | 5 | (had) bounced |
| 3 | (had) shouted | | |

| | | | |
|---|---|---|---|
| 1 | had stolen | 3 | (had) reported |
| 2 | had gone / went | 4 | heard |
| | | 5 | (had) answered |

3 1d, 2c, 3a, 4b
4 1 He decided to rob the bank.
2 He realised that he had left the note in the bank.

3 He had left the car keys in the bank too.
4 They took the car keys and opened the car then went to the address of the car owner.

5 2 would not have gone / had not left
3 had not gone / would not have forgotten
4 had not hidden / would not have made
5 would not have called / had brought
6 had not reported / would not have known
7 would not have been able / had not found

## Writing

1 1 additionally, furthermore, moreover, in addition, as well as, what is more
2 nevertheless, nonetheless, in spite of, yet, although, however, despite
2 1 people with access to a company's money
2 three
3 better financial rules and regulations
3 **Suggested answers**
1 additionally
2 moreover
3 furthermore
4 what is more
5 In addition
4 **Example answer**
The majority believe tagging is a positive development. However, evidence shows that counselling is much better.
5 **Suggested answer**
It is often a topic of debate whether education or imprisonment is more effective in reforming criminals. Should we punish them for their behaviour or try to teach them the benefits of living within the law?

It is clear that we need to remove dangerous criminals from society for the safety of others. Nevertheless, some less serious offenders may not benefit from going to prison. Although they need to be punished in some way, mixing with other criminals might teach them new crimes, and these contacts may continue after they leave prison. A jail sentence is supposed to act as a deterrent to further crime, but the statistics do not support this, as many offenders return to prison time after time.

The government has considered many alternatives such as tagging and community service, however, these have not proved to be much more effective. In my opinion, these schemes are simply a way for the government to save money, as keeping a person in prison is very expensive. In spite of this, I think that for young offenders such as graffiti artists, such measures might be suitable.

In the USA, offenders doing community service have to wear bright orange uniforms so that people know who they are. It may be true that this public shaming may help people to identify the criminals in future, yet I believe it is unnecessarily cruel.

On the whole, I would like to see the government focus its efforts on social education in schools, thus preventing young people from becoming criminals in the first place. Programmes which require students to work together to solve a problem can teach them the benefits of building society rather than destroying it. I feel these projects should also take place outside the classroom, although they would need to be carefully supervised by specially trained people.

To sum up, I believe that prevention is better than cure, and that showing young people the advantages of cooperating with others is the key to preventing crime in our society.

## Vocabulary

1 
| | | | |
|---|---|---|---|
| 1 | thief | 5 | truant |
| 2 | mugger | 6 | burglar |
| 3 | vandal | 7 | robber |
| 4 | shoplifter | 8 | criminal |

2 
| | | | |
|---|---|---|---|
| 1 | tagged | 4 | fine |
| 2 | community service | 5 | probation |
| 3 | excluded | | |

## Revise for IELTS

1 a underline the important words
b read the passage quickly
c look for similar words and phrases in the passage and questions
d look for opposite words
e make sure the information is in the passage
2 problem, solution, evaluation
3 three: background, statement, question

# Unit 8
## Study skills

1 Student A: course
Student B: social life

## Reading

1 1 No (lines 6 – 7)
2 No (line 10)
3 Yes (line 20)
4 Not given
5 No (lines 46 – 47)

2 
| | | | |
|---|---|---|---|
| 1 | good nor evil | 6 | successful |
| 2 | globalisation | 7 | everyone else |

3 transport costs   8 exploitative way
4 efficient   9 production
5 supplier   10 internal pricing

## Language study

**1** 1 A place where you can buy medicine is called a chemist's.
2 A person who deals with money at a university is called a bursar.
3 The only shop which is open until 11 p.m. is on Richmond Road.
4 *Music Giant* – is that the shop which sells CDs?
5 The new treasurer is someone who is very careful with money.

**2** 1 Jane took me to see the shop where she worked / the shop she worked in last term.
2 Many companies which were owned by the state have been sold.
3 The workers who are employed at Sydney textiles are worried about their company.
4 The manager who got a big pay rise was interviewed on television.
5 Wei Wei has sold the course books (which) she bought last year.

**3** 1 The protest in Seattle, which was held against the World Trade Organisation, was not very peaceful.
2 Sales of Fair Trade products, which have been produced since the 1960s, have been rising steadily.
3 The President of the World Bank, who is 60 today, is in China for talks.
4 John Maynard Keynes, who died in 1946, was a world famous economist.
5 Adelaide, where I went to University, will hold a big trade show this year.

**4 Suggested answers**
1 Tao, Johnny, Anna, Demet and Carlos are students, all of whom are studying at the University of Bradford.
2 A number of them are taking Engineering.
3 Some of them have a car.
4 Many of them are in the film society.
5 Most of them have part-time jobs.

## Listening

**1** 1 four   5 textiles
2 bananas   6 four
3 Cuba   7 negative
4 its airline

**2** 1 protecting domestic industries
2 tax
3 more expensive
4 complete ban
5 unofficial
6 money or tax

7 uncompetitive
8 quantity
9 unfair
10 employment
11 unfair competition
12 new industry
13 raise revenue
14 flow of trade

## Writing

**1** 1 A multinational can be defined as a company which has branches all over the world.
2 Deflation is a process in which the economy slows down and prices drop.
3 An accountant is defined as someone who prepares financial records for a company.

**2** Title 2

**3** 1 This is due to a total external debt
2 this resulted in many countries owing more than the original amount
3 causing developing countries to sell state companies
4 As a consequence of cuts in public spending
5 because banks had too much money

**4 Suggested answer**

Over recent years the wealth gap between developed and developing nations has grown wider. This is in spite of large amounts of aid from developed countries and large loans from organisations like the International Monetary Fund and the World Bank. I would like to argue in this essay that developing nations need more than just money, but that at the same time unlimited free trade is not the answer.

Developed countries have been giving developing countries money in two basic ways: aid and loans. Unfortunately this has led to two major problems. Firstly, aid can cause a culture where a country depends on money from outside instead of creating its own wealth. Secondly, loans given by international organisations had high rates of interest and very bad conditions attached to them, so that countries which received these loans could never pay them back or could only pay them back at a high cost to their own welfare system and economy. It is obvious that the kind of aid and loans given in the past have not helped but in fact have contributed to the problem.

Therefore we need to look at international trade as a way of helping developing nations. Many people argue that globalisation is a way of creating wealth around the world and helping poorer nations. However, in reality globalisation has resulted in rich nations becoming richer and poorer nations remaining poor. I believe that this is not due to the effect of international trade, but because of the rules of global trade – rules invented by the developed countries. For example, developing countries are encouraged to drop taxes and tariffs on companies from outside their countries like multinational companies. As a consequence, their own companies cannot compete and go out of business. At the same time, however, developed countries put tariffs on cheap goods like clothes and textiles from developing countries in order to protect their own domestic industries.

In conclusion, I agree in part that international trade is the best way of helping developing nations, but that we need to rewrite the rules of international trade before it can really benefit these countries.

## Vocabulary

**1** 
| Across | Down |
| --- | --- |
| 5 inflation | 1 investor |
| 7 data | 2 capital |
| 9 subsidy | 3 commodity |
| 10 income | 4 prosperity |
| | 6 sustainable |
| | 8 tariff |

## Pronunciation

**1** 1 defining   4 non-defining
2 non-defining   5 non-defining
3 defining

## Revise for IELTS

1 Let's take a closer look at … / Let's explore these … in more detail … / I'd like to turn now to … / I'd like to move on to … / I'm going to go into more detail about …
2 That's enough about … / So much for …
3 In effect … / To sum up today's lecture …

# Unit 9
## Study skills

career opportunity; executive committee; daily routine; business consultant; flight attendant; ten-year contract; fire fighter; holding company; ethnic minority; internet technician; police officer

# Reading

**1** A 2, B 3, C 4, D 1

**2** 1 Y (line 3), 2 NG, 3 N (lines 9 – 10),
4 N (line 22), 5 Y (line 28),
6 Y (lines 52 – 54), 7 NG, 8 Y (line
57), 9 N (lines 74 – 75)

# Language study

**1** 1 didn't use to    5 would
2 would    6 used to
3 would    7 used to
4 didn't use to

**2** 1 didn't use to be able to
2 used to stay
3 used to have to
4 used to work
5 used to be employed
6 used to have
7 didn't use to have
8 didn't use to happen
9 didn't use to be allowed to
10 used to be

**3** 1 Did she use to work in Australia?
2 Did you use to live in China?
3 Did you use to go to the University
of Melbourne?
4 Did you use to visit the library?
5 Did you use to own a car?

**4** 1 told, 2 say, 3 told, 4 told, 5 said

**5** 1 She said that it was hers.
2 Hilda said he was going to meet her
there the next day.
3 The landlady told me that she had
left the week before.
4 Marta said that there was another
train to Paris at 10.30 that evening.
5 She asked me if I would still be
there the following week.
6 The secretary said she was sure that
she had left it there that morning.
7 The chairperson said that those rules
and regulations were outdated.
8 She told him that she resigned right
there and then.
9 She asked if she could have another
one of those biscuits.
10 Mrs Chan said that she would see
me there the following Tuesday.

**6** 1 would read    8 she would be able
2 was worried    9 that evening
3 couldn't    10 had been
   planning    11 that night
4 had just had    12 would try
5 had missed    13 did, he would
6 the day before 14 that week
7 was taking her

# Listening

**1** 1 monopolise    4 self-made
2 reluctant    5 sheltered
3 aviation    6 advocate

**2** 1 B, 2 A, 3 D, 4 C

**3** 1 aviator    5 approves

2 employed    6 exclusive
3 in charge    7 supported
4 received    8 disapprove

# Writing

**1** In the past 100 years, the role of women
in society has changed. Give some
reasons for these changes and say how
you feel about them. Include any
relevant examples from your own
experience.

**2** 1 One illustration of this
2 like
3 Another example
4 like
5 as can be demonstrated by
6 for instance
7 If one considers

**3** **Suggested answer**

Since the beginning of the twentieth
century women have fought for equal
rights and opportunities in society,
gaining the right to vote and the right
to equal pay and employment
opportunities (in many countries).
However, even in countries that have
equal rights, few women reach positions
of real power within business, law or the
government. In this essay I would like
to look at some reasons for this and
suggest some ways forward.

In countries with labour laws that make
discrimination between men and
women illegal, discrimination still exists
in terms of pay and promotion. In the
UK, for example, women earn on
average 20% less than men. While this
is serious, perhaps a more serious sign of
inequality is that women are not as
frequently promoted to top
management positions as men. In
Sweden, only 1.5% of women reach
senior management, and in the USA
only 11% of women reach these
positions. There are many reasons for
this, to give one illustration, the most
common reason given is that women
break their careers to have children.
However, this does not explain the
problem as facilities like nurseries and
creches can be provided to help. Other
explanations are that women are said to
be not as aggressive as men. This can be
shown in the workplace where men
compete against each other. However, it
is argued that most women prefer co-
operation to competition and do worse
than men in companies with a
competitive culture.

In my opinion there are a number of
ways of dealing with this. The most
obvious way is better regulation of the
workplace by governments. The second
way is positive discrimination: giving
people the chances that they do not

have because of discrimination – this
has already been used in the USA and
in Britain. Finally, because industry is
changing, teamwork and networking are
become more important. These are
things that women are better at than
men, so in the future it will make
business sense to promote women to
senior management positions as they are
better at these things than men.

# Vocabulary

**1** 2 flight attendant
3 firefighter
4 chair(person)
5 homemaker

**2** 1 management styles
2 double standards
3 sabbatical year
4 human resources
5 deep-rooted prejudice
6 performance evaluation
7 good-humoured
8 interpersonal skills
9 equal opportunities
10 middle-management

# Pronunciation

**1** 1 applicant, prejudice
2 performance, resources, commission
3 educational, university, interpersonal

# Revise for IELTS

1 mind maps
2 two minutes
3 to avoid referring to gender

# Unit 10
## Study skills

**1** 1 I've got so much to study … and so
little time
2 I don't know where to begin
3 I'm bored with books
4 I think I understand it
5 There's too much to remember
6 I like to study in bed
7 I'm going to stay up all night until I
understand this

## Listening

**1** a4, b7, c3, d6, e2, f5, g1

**2** 1 C, 2 A, 3 B, 4 C, 5 B, 6 B

## Language study

**1** 1 explain    5 claim
2 agree    6 conclude
3 urge    7 summarise
4 suggest

**2**
1 agree  4 urge
2 conclude  5 explain
3 suggest  6 claim

**3** 2 He concluded that GM crops were the future solution to feeding people in the developing world.
3 He suggested that she tried crop rotation to control the weeds instead of chemicals.
4 He urged her to try organically-produced beef.
5 She explained (to them) that if they rotated their crops that way the pests wouldn't be able to stay in the same area the following year.
6 He claimed that GM food was totally safe.

**4** In the meeting yesterday to debate the introduction of GM crops, Gordon Smith urged the prime minister <u>to commission</u> an independent scientific report. The prime minister insisted <u>that</u> the report was already under way. Mr Smith then recommended <u>having</u> a second team of scientists to monitor the first group. The prime minister asserted <u>that it</u> was not necessary. Mr Smith went on to suggest <u>that the government were</u> putting pressure on the commission to produce a favourable report, but the prime minister pointed <u>out</u> that this was impossible because the government had no position on whether GM crops should be introduced or not.

# Reading

**1** 1 NG,
2 T (line 8 – 9),
3 T (lines 12 – 13),
4 F (line 26),
5 F (line 29),
6 T (line 36)

**2** 1 food industry
2 millions of dollars
3 starchy snacks
4 low-carb
5 low-fat
6 lighter oils
7 animal fats
8 cholesterol
9 heart disease
10 calorie-controlled
11 low-carb
12 high-protein
13 blood-sugar levels
14 cancer
15 range of food
16 personal preferences
17 range of options

# Writing

**1** 1 in other words, to put it differently, again
2 rather than, alternatively, to look at it from another point of view

**2** paragraph B: rather than, in other words
paragraph C: alternatively, to put it another way
paragraph E: rather than

**3** 1 D, 2 A, 3 F, 4 B, 5 H, 6 E

**4** Some people believe that making <u>donations of food aid</u> to <u>developing countries</u> does <u>more harm than good</u>. <u>To what extent</u> do you <u>agree</u> with this opinion?

**5** 1 F, 2 B, 3 D, 4 E, 5 G, 6 A, 7 C

**6 Possible answers**
2 drinking milk or fruit juice
3 we could go out for a coffee
4 I'm not very sporty
5 eating fruit and vegetables keeps us well

**7 Example answers**
2 To put it differently, you should drink milk, water or tea.
3 In other words, it is not cooked with herbs and spices.
4 To look at it from another angle, they should eat more apples and carrots.
5 In other words, they usually eat meals off a tray in front of the television.

# Vocabulary

**1** courses: starter, dessert, main course, side dish

how food tastes: spicy, savoury, sweet, delicious, flavourless

ways of cooking food: roast, grilled, boiled

**2** 1 go Dutch  4 insist
2 on me  5 get this
3 my treat

# Pronunciation

**1** When the final /t/ or /d/ sound is followed by a consonant, we do not pronounce the sound.

# Revise for IELTS

**1** a reading and underlining key words
b looking for words like *believe, agree, oppose*
c look for phrases that introduce an opinion
d be careful with statements that give an opposite opinion before the writer gives their own opinion

# Unit 11
## Study skills

**2** 1 If he does not get the score he needs, he knows when the next test is.

2 One month
3 Speaking – he is trying to do lots of conversation and interview practice

# Reading

**1** 1 A, 2 A, 3 B, 4 C, 5 B

**2** 1 GGW, 2 GGW, 3 GG, 4 GGW, 5 CBP

**3** 1 grassland has been turned into a dust bowl, airports have been closed in Japan and Korea, it formed an orange haze in the USA
2 deforestation, drought, over-exploitation of water
3 straw mats, chemicals

**4** 1 crops  4 ecotourism
2 Chinese pine  5 training centre
3 wood burning  6 waste-water

# Language study

**1** 1 transitive  3 transitive
2 transitive  4 intransitive

**2** 1 make up for
2 drawing down on
3 put up with
4 keep up with

**3** 1 will have emitted
2 will have risen
3 will be living
4 will be recycling
5 will have become

# Listening

**1** 1 A, 2 C, 3 C, 4 B

**2** 1 Canada
2 Australia/United States
3 Britain
4 Australia
5 United States
6 Britain

**3** 1 buried/burnt
2 (metal) lids, (plastic) tops, (plastic) labels
3 light bulbs, drinking glasses
4 libraries, charity shops
5 handsets, batteries and chargers

# Writing

**1** <u>Climate change</u> can be more effectively tackled by <u>governments rather than individuals</u>.
To what <u>extent</u> do you <u>agree or disagree</u> with this statement?

**2** 1 I, 2 I, 3 G, 4 I, 5 G, 6 I, 7 G, 8 G, 9 G, 10 I

**3** 1, 2, 3, 5, 6, 8, 10

**4** 1 its  5 it
2 they  6 them
3 them  7 these
4 it  8 this

## Vocabulary

**1**
1 energy
2 source
3 climate change
4 fossil fuels
5 diesel
6 greenhouse gases
7 global warming
8 extreme
9 droughts
10 hurricanes
11 irreversible
12 renewable
13 resources
14 ecosystems

## Pronunciation

**1**
1 ocean, global, ecosystem
2 resource, storm, warming
3 government, flood, hurricane
4 conservation, policy

## Revise for IELTS

1 20 minutes / 40 minutes
2 Yes.

# Unit 12

## Study skills

**1** A 2, B 4, C 1, D 5, E 6, F 3

**2**
1 true
2 false – if you arrive late you should talk to the invigilator, but you may not be allowed to take the test
3 false – you can only take in pens, pencils and erasers you need to do the test
4 false
5 true
6 false – the invigilator will not explain any question to you
7 false – you cannot leave the room without asking the invigilator or until all the papers have been collected and you are told you can leave
8 false – mobile phones must be switched off and left in the place for bags and coats. You may be disqualified if your phone is on
9 true – you could be disqualified if you try to do this
10 true – you could be disqualified if you try to do this
11 false

## Language study

**1**
1 relaxing
2 interesting
3 exhausted
4 petrifying
5 delighted
6 boring

**2**
1 Had I not had my own computer, I wouldn't have been able to work from home.
2 A common pattern of work now is home-working.
3 Never before have the areas of biotechnology, computing and software production been so

important.
4 Rarely do people nowadays remain in the same job during their working lives.
5 No longer will people without computing skills find it easy to find work.
6 Seldom will assembly and repetitive work be done by humans in future.

## Reading

**1** 1 C, 2 B, 3 C, 4 B

**2**
1 family
2 structure
3 themes
4 information
5 review

**3**
1 workload
2 socially
3 size
4 course structure

## Listening

**1**
1 positive    b, d, e, f, h, j
2 negative    a, c, g, i

**2**
1 b
2 a
3 f
4 d
5 h
6 c
7 j
8 i
9 e
10 g

**3**
1 impression
2 eye contact
3 relaxed
4 paying attention
5 tilt your head
6 posture
7 fidgeting
8 role model
9 watching people
10 gestures
11 'similar to me'

## Writing

1 Your college principal has invited you and your classmates to attend an end of course party. He has also asked for suggestions for a suitable present for your course tutor.
You are now writing a letter to the principal.
In your letter:
ı thank him for the invitation
ı suggest a suitable present for your tutor
ı offer to help organize the purchase of the present.

**2** 1 T, 2 F, 3 F

**3** line 3   enjoyed → enjoyable (word class)
line 5   interested in (missing word)
line 5   i → I (punctuation)
line 6   intresting → interesting (spelling)

line 7   delighted → delightful (word class)
line 9   refectery → refectory (spelling)
line 10  looking at them (missing word)
line 12  happy to arrange (missing word)
line 12  friday → Friday (punctuation)
line 14  book so that (missing word)
line 14  will he → he will (word order)
line 15  sugestion → suggestion (spelling)
line 16  invitaton → invitation (spelling)

## Vocabulary

**1**

## Pronunciation

**1**
1 2 syllables – farewell, milk round, boring, wound up
2 3 syllables – challenging, interested, delightful, wonderful, barbecue
3 4 syllables – petrifying, enjoyable, graduation, ceremony, invitation

**2**
1 interested
2 delightful
3 farewell
4 petrifying
5 enjoyable
6 barbecue
7 boring
8 graduation
9 wonderful
10 ceremony
11 invitation
12 milk round
13 challenging
14 wound up

## Revise for IELTS

1 In other words, to put it another way, so what you are asking is
2 Could you explain what you mean by …? Can you give me an example of what you mean?
3 No
4 Yes
5 American English and British English

# Listening passages

## Unit 1

### Track 1

Hello and welcome. My name's Carolyn Tan. Just as there are a great number of different courses and places to study here, the teaching methods used and the skills you need will vary, depending on the subject you study and the college or university you attend. All courses vary, but most include some of the teaching methods I'm going to talk about today. Generally speaking, in some subjects, you will have timetabled classes for most of the week. In others you may only have a few hours timetabled and will be expected to work independently for a substantial amount of time. Working independently is crucial at university. I'm going to go over the three main types of teaching method you will have here. These are lectures, seminars and tutorials. There are other methods that you will come across like workshops, group work and practical work, but I'll describe the three main types for now. I'll briefly describe what they are and try to give you some helpful advice in dealing with them.

Let's start by looking at lectures. These are large classes, usually lasting around one hour, where a lecturer (or tutor) talks about a subject and the students take notes. On some courses there can be over a hundred students in a lecture. Unfortunately, there is usually little or no opportunity to ask questions during the lecture. Lectures are usually intended to do three things. Firstly, to guide you through the course by explaining the main points of a topic, secondly to introduce new topics for further study or debate and thirdly to give you the most up-to-date information that may not be included in textbooks. So as you can see, it's essential to go to lectures. Of course, you need to take notes in lectures. Remember, you don't need to write down everything the lecturer says – try to concentrate on the main points and important details. Most lecturers use stories, examples and even jokes to illustrate a point, and you shouldn't write these down. When you take notes in lectures, abbreviations and symbols for common words and terms can help you write faster. If there is something you don't understand, make a note to ask after the lecture or in a tutorial. Most students try to write up their notes after a lecture. It's a good idea to try to be organised – keep your notes from your lectures in order in a file – but don't just file the notes away until your exams, read through them regularly as this will help you with your revision. It's really important to go over your lectures. As an international student, the lecturer will recognise that you may need more help in lectures and that you may want to record the lecture on a digital recorder. If you do want to do this, ask the lecturer's permission first – they will usually agree. Finally, don't worry if you find it difficult to understand the lecturer at first. This will get easier as you get used to their style and as your English improves.

Okay, that's enough about lectures. Let's have a look at seminars now. Seminars are smaller classes where students and a tutor discuss a topic and they often last about the same time, if not longer than lectures. You will know in advance what the topic is, and the tutor will usually ask some students to prepare a short presentation for discussion. Seminars are usually meant to encourage debate about an issue. This means different opinions will be expressed by the tutor and students. The aim is not for students to be told the correct answer, but to understand different arguments and make judgements about them. This process helps you learn to analyse topics critically. Some international students find that seminars can be a bit frightening, especially if they are not used to this kind of teaching. Don't worry. Many other students feel the same at first. Participating actively in seminars is an important part of the learning process, so try to contribute, even if it seems difficult at first. It is best to do some reading before each seminar, so that you are familiar with the topic and can follow and contribute to the discussion. It may help you to make notes before the seminar of any points you would like to make. If you are having difficulty in seminars, discuss this with your tutor.

And finally I'll give you information on tutorials. Tutorials are meetings between a tutor and an individual student or small group of students. These usually last between fifteen and thirty minutes. In a tutorial the tutor will give you advice and guidance on a piece of work you are doing or a piece of work you have completed, or even a problem you may be having with a topic or with study methods. You should try to ask questions during tutorials about your work or about topics raised in lectures and seminars. Well, that's all for teaching methods. I'll go on now to talk about the different kinds of examinations ...

## Track 2

It's essential to go to lectures.

It's really important to go over your lectures.

Working independently is crucial at university.

# Unit 2

## Track 3

A: Hi, I'm here to pay my University fees.

B: Hello, right. Now is that both course fees and accommodation fees or is it one or the other?

A: I'd like to pay my course fees at the moment and I'll pay for my accommodation later this week.

B: Very well. Let's start with the course you are on.

A: I'm with the School of Management, with the department of marketing.

B: All right, and which course are you taking, is it a short course, part-time or full-time course?

A: I'm full-time, postgraduate.

B: That's part-time postgraduate.

A: No, sorry, I'm full-time.

B: Okay. Now what kind of degree is it?

A: It's a master of arts.

B: So that's MA in international management.

A: Actually it's management and marketing.

B: Do you have a course code for that?

A: Yes, it's here on my acceptance letter: it's PMKTMAN.

B: Could you repeat that for me please?

A: Sure, PMKTMAN.

B: Right. Let me just do a quick search for that. Here we are – course fees – £10,000 if you pay in one instalment, and if you pay in monthly instalments it's £10,250.

A: How much is that per month?

B: We take the first £300 as a non-returnable deposit.

A: So that means that if I don't finish the course, I can't get my money back.

B: Well, you can't get the first £300 back. If you can't finish the course due to a good reason – for example, if you become ill, we can usually give you most of your course fee back.

A: And after that?

B: After that you can pay each month in instalments of £1,000.

A: Okay, that sounds reasonable – I think I'll pay by monthly instalments.

B: Right, and how would you like to pay?

A: Can I pay by debit card?

B: Yes, of course – as long as you have enough money in your account. Let me take a few details from you first. What's your full name?

A: My name's Per Jensen.

B: Could you tell me how to spell that?

A: It's P-E-R J-E-N-S-E-N.

B: Okay, and your university number is …

A: My university number is UB606 133.

B: That's UB606 133. Now, would you like to pay your monthly instalments by direct debit?

A: You mean that the bank will pay automatically at a certain date every month?

B: Yes, that's right, so you don't have to come here every month.

A: That sounds good.

B: In that case you'll need a few details from us to take to the bank.

A: Okay.

B: So, you will need to make the payment to the university, sort code 40-84-15.

A: Can you tell me that sort code again please?

B: 40-84-15, and the account number is 888 00 16 60.

A: Okay, and all I need to do is to give these details to my bank.

B: That's correct.

A: Well, thanks very much.

B: Wait a minute – you need your receipt, to prove you've paid. Here you are.

A: Thanks, bye.

## Track 4

transfer

exchange

convert

statement

balance

payment

bankrupt

withdraw

account

purchase

# Unit 3

## Track 5

The city of Budapest, which is the capital of Hungary, has an excellent public transport system. It is also extremely good value for money. The variety of transport types in Budapest is surprising, and one travel pass enables the purchaser to use most of them. Passes may be bought for a range of specified periods from a single day to a month, and a monthly pass costs 6,250 Hungarian Forints. This may sound like a lot, but in fact it is under 26 Euros – for a whole month of unrestricted travel within the city. These passes are on sale in railway terminals, metro stations and newsagents.

One of the most scenic routes in the centre of the city is the number two tram, which travels along the bank of the River Danube, offering views of the impressive citadel and castle on the other side. The tram then goes past the main market and around the spectacular Houses of Parliament. Alternatively, there are many buses and trolleybuses which make frequent journeys all over the city. It is never necessary to wait more than a few minutes for transport. Buses with a red number are express routes, and make fewer stops than those with black numbers.

There is also an underground railway, or Metro, which is popular with commuters. There are three metro lines operating from central locations, and one of these is the oldest in continental Europe. The Metro operates from 4.30 a.m. to 11.00 p.m., but during the night, buses follow the same routes above ground. To reach the surrounding areas outside Budapest, the travel pass also entitles you to travel on the suburban HÉV train line. Thus travellers can reach towns such as Szentendre, a popular tourist destination.

Budapest also has a range of special vehicles which require separate tickets, as they are not included in the travel pass. One of these is the funicular, which operates on Castle Hill, on the Buda side of the river. The ticket to go up is more expensive than the one to come down! Another is the chairlift, similar to those used by skiers. This ascends 262 metres to the look-out point on János Hill, but it is not recommended unless you have a good head for heights. There is even a special railway staffed by children, which goes through the woods and hills of Buda for 11 km. On weekends, the children's railway operates a steam train. The drivers, however, are qualified adults, and the children are carefully supervised.

The city of Budapest, therefore, presents an example to the rest of the capital cities of the world. If all large cities had such cheap and efficient public transport systems, congestion and pollution caused by traffic in the city centre could be greatly reduced, and today's cities would be more pleasant and less stressful to live in.

## Track 6

1 travelled

2 invited

3 climbed

4 arrived

5 boarded

6 dropped

7 missed

8 picked

9 wished

10 sailed

11 carried

12 performed

13 worked

14 mended

15 entered

16 produced

17 recorded

18 invested

19 listened

20 tested

# Unit 4

## Track 7

**Presenter**: Well, it's the beginning of the digital age. And technology is all set to completely revolutionise the way we watch TV, videos and DVDs and play computer games at home. Here to tell us more about how we will be spending our leisure time at home in future is Anna Szabò.

**Anna Szabò**: Hello. Yes, there will be huge changes in the way we use television, radio and new media in future. By this I mean we will be able to do what we want, where we want and when we want. The result is that our homes will increasingly become home theatres. And all our entertainment at home will be available at the touch of a button! Now most home entertainment these days is delivered over wires. But this is changing thanks to high-speed broadband. Downloading will become easier and studios will eventually release movies, songs and video games directly to the consumer. So, for example, instead of a film opening on the big screen and eventually appearing on television, video and the Internet, it can appear in all formats at once. This means that we will have more choice and control over the media we use.

**Presenter**: So, how will we use this media in our homes in future?

**Anna Szabò**: There will be big changes in how we watch video and television. Several research groups and companies are trying to add depth to TV and other video displays in the form of a third dimension.

**Presenter**: So television and video screens will have depth. What do you mean by 'depth' exactly? Do you mean 3-D – like a hologram?

**Anna Szabò**: That's right. When we say that a hologram has three dimensions, it means that we can see not only up and down and left and right but forwards and backwards too. When we talk about dimensions we call forwards and backwards 'depth'. So when we say that a hologram has three dimensions it means we can see up and down and left and right, just like a picture or photo. But we can also look 'into' the hologram because the image it contains has depth.

**Presenter**: So instead of watching films on a flat screen, we will be watching them in 3-D.

**Anna Szabò**: Absolutely. Well, as we live in a 3-D world we shouldn't really be watching television and films in 2-D and the technology to make this happen is already there. 3-D screens are being developed which can be placed throughout the house, even in busy areas of our homes like doorways and halls. Now, these screens appear to float in air. So in the future, 3-D holographic images will be sent into our homes and we will be able to experience the action as if it is taking place right in front of our eyes.

**Presenter**: So, the action won't just look real. It will be real. Incredible! How does this technology work?

**Anna Szabò**: Well, to get true 3-D each of your eyes has to see a slightly different image. 3-D screens interweave multiple images in vertical stripes using special coatings and filters built into the screen. This means that each eye sees a different set of stripes. These screens are called lenticular screens. Now these screens are easy to produce and some laptop PCs and cell phones already have them. However, lenticular screens do have one disadvantage. The strain on the eyes and brain of putting together a 3-D image from two flat ones can result in headaches and dizziness. But a few companies have developed a hologram 3-D display which does not cause these problems. Instead of building images then leaving them to the brain to put together, holograms create a whole image that reaches the eye exactly the way light from a real object does. You can even walk part of the way round a holographic image to see side and back views – just as you would do if the object was right in front of you. Twin holograms will let a couple watch two different programmes on the same screen even if they sit next to each other on the living room sofa.

**Presenter**: So no more arguing about which programme to watch!

**Anna Szabò**: That's right. Patio screens are being developed too.

**Presenter**: Patio screens? What are they exactly?

**Anna Szabò**: Well, a patio screen is a big inflatable screen which means you can take it outside your home and watch a film in your garden! Some patio screens are even equipped with DVD players and some new ones may even have a wireless connection.

**Presenter**: Amazing developments there. Well, join us after the break when we will be talking to …

## Track 8

here to tell us more

you can even walk part of the way

when we talk about dimensions

# Unit 5

## Track 9

Today I'm going to talk about the city of Barcelona and its architecture. First, the city.

Barcelona is a city of some one and a half million people. It is a port, situated on the north-east coast of Spain in the province of Catalunya. The people speak Catalan as their native language, but most are also fluent in Castilian Spanish, and some speak English too. The city centre is surrounded by a ring road which encloses a grid, with two major roads running diagonally across it. These are the Avenidas Diagonal and Meridiana. Probably the most famous street in Barcelona is La Rambla, which connects the Plaça de Catalunya in the town centre to the statue of Columbus on the water's edge. All along the centre of this wide boulevard are stalls selling flowers and artistic works.

Barcelona was founded by the Carthaginians, from modern-day Tunisia in North Africa. It grew under the influence of the Roman Empire, later becoming the capital of Spain. Under strong government it expanded its trade, exporting cloth to other Mediterranean ports, and establishing itself as a financial centre. It went into decline after 1400, and in 1640 it was the centre of the Catalan revolution against King Philip IV of Spain. Now it is considered by many to be the cultural centre of Spain, and the Olympic Games were held there in 1992.

Now to the architecture. Throughout the city, there are many fine buildings: churches, cathedrals, markets and squares, which date back to the thirteenth century. One very fine square which can be entered from La Rambla is the Plaça Reial, or Royal Square. This was built by Molina in the 19th century. Seven narrow passages lead into a large central area which is surrounded by two-storey buildings. Most of the ground floor is occupied by restaurants and bars, and it is traditionally a place of music and entertainment.

It is impossible to talk about the architecture of Barcelona without mentioning Gaudi, who dominated the scene from the 1880s until his death in 1926. His style was unique, a decorative form of art nouveau, the style of the 1920s and 30s in Europe. It was based on organic, natural forms which often seem to defy the qualities of the materials they are made from. I will mention just three of his best-known works today.

The first is Guell Palace. This was built for the Count of Guell, one of Gaudi's main supporters. The building features two arched gates, which lead into the stable area. Inside are two circular staircases – one for people, and the other for horses. The ground floor is built of brick, but there is also much natural stone used in the construction. The roof is quite fantastic, with brightly coloured sculptures built around the chimneys and ventilation shafts.

Another project commissioned by Guell is the park named after him. This was meant to be a garden city with fifty houses, but in fact only two were ever finished. The influence of nature is strong in the cave-like spaces and animal figures, and again much use has been made of brilliantly-coloured surfaces.

But the greatest of Gaudi's works is still under construction, and it is not expected to be finished until 2041. He began work on this cathedral, known as *la Sagrada Familia* (Church of the Holy Family) in 1882, which means that it will have taken 159 years to complete. The finished building will have eighteen towers, the highest being 170 metres high. The building will be 95 metres long by 60 metres wide, and it will hold 13,000 people – a truly impressive monument to Gaudi's great genius.

And that's all we have time for today. Next week, we'll look at some of Gaudi's smaller projects, and also his furniture designs. Please make sure that you complete your assignment on le Corbusier by this coming Friday.

## Track 10

*Examples:*   My brother lives in Germany.

          I owe you a visit.

1   Go and tell him to come here.
2   Her family come from Boston.
3   Who are you?
4   Where is the umbrella?
5   I like to visit other cities.
6   He's moved to another town.
7   Los Angeles means 'the angels'.
8   Clear skies over Melbourne.

# Unit 6

## Track 11

**Interviewer**: Well, the 150th edition has just come out. It's sold 32 million copies. Yes, that's right – 32 million! What is it? Roget's Thesaurus! Now, Roget's Thesaurus is a type of dictionary in which words with similar meanings are grouped together. The word 'thesaurus' comes from Greek and means 'Treasure House'. So, to tell us more about Roget's Thesaurus is linguist Dr Cindy Chenner. Now then, Cindy, we know Roget classified the English language but what do we know about the man himself?

**Cindy Chenner**: Well, Mr Roget – or to give him his full name – Peter Mark Roget – was a very interesting man indeed. He grew up in London, he was French and spent his early life in a French community there. He later travelled all the way from London to Edinburgh to study medicine at the University there and graduated when he was nineteen years old. And he later went on to become a founder of Manchester Medical School.

**Interviewer**: So his life focussed around his career as a doctor.

**Cindy Chenner**: Well, actually no. Roget had a very wide range of interests indeed. In fact, he was a writer and wrote about many topics such as bees, the kaleidoscope and even perception and feeling in animals. And he was an inventor too. In fact, in 1814 he invented an early version of the slide rule.

**Interviewer**: The slide rule?

**Cindy Chenner**: Yes, the device that can calculate numbers. Then ten years later he developed a prototype for the cine camera. And he also got involved in a range of different projects. For example, he became head of a commission investigating London's water supply and he developed a method of water filtration through sand. And he was involved in the area of education. He was one of the founders of London University. And do you play chess by any chance, Mark?

**Interviewer**: Yes, I do.

**Cindy Chenner**: Well, Roget invented the travelling chess set. So next time you are playing a game of chess on a train, you have Mr Roget to thank!

**Interviewer**: So, how did he actually find the time to classify the English Language?

**Cindy Chenner**: Well, he only turned his full attention to the Thesaurus when he retired – and that was when he was in his seventies!

**Interviewer**: So what inspired him to write the Thesaurus?

**Cindy Chenner**: Well, Roget believed that he should bring as much happiness and knowledge to the greatest number of people. So, during his career as a doctor, he gave free treatment to patients who couldn't afford to pay. We also know that he set up a clinic to help poor people to recover from operations and serious illnesses. Basically, he wrote the Thesaurus to help people learn. He aimed to help those who needed practice in writing. He believed that writing skills would help people become more independent and lead happier lives.

**Interviewer**: How popular is the Thesaurus today?

**Cindy Chenner**: Well, it was first published in 1852 and it has never been out of print since! In fact the book has become more popular with each edition that comes out! The invention of the crossword puzzle in 1913 certainly helped to increase the sales figures though! I think the main reason why it is so popular is that it is thematic. So you can come across words that you had never even thought of when you began looking for the word in the first place.

**Interviewer**: Thanks Cindy. Now join us again after this short break …

## Track 12

the future of English
New Englishes are appearing
core speakers
key grammar areas

# Unit 7

## Track 13

Hello everyone, I'd like to go over some simple security measures today. As you all know, there have been a few small incidents with students' possessions being lost or stolen and as the Student Representative for Middlesex hall of residence, I'd like to remind everyone of a few simple things we can do to make our accommodation safer for everyone and to remind everyone of the security measures already in place.

First of all I'd like to go over what security measures are already in or around the halls of residence. As you turn off the road into Middlesex Hall there is a security barrier for people arriving by car. Students, or anyone else for that matter, have to report to security through the speaker before they can even enter the car park. Once they are in the car park we have CCTV – that's closed circuit television – linked directly to the security office so that anyone coming into the front entrance via the car park can be seen by the person on duty. We also have cameras around the hall of residence. The film from the CCTV is kept by security in case there is a problem and we need to send the film to the police to help identify the person. So, barriers and CCTV. In addition to these there is security lighting in the car park and around the hall of residence which is on from night to morning.

These security measures are there to help, but the really important thing is the front entrance. At the front entrance is a keypad lock. Now as you all know, to open this you need your student card and the four-digit security code. As you also know, you should not give this code to anyone you do not know, and you should never let anyone into the hall of residence. Remember that for all the security measures we take, if you let someone into the hall, then anything we do to keep students' possessions safe will not help. After the front door, we have the reception desk. Now, this is manned 24 hours a day, but the security guard has a lot to do and may not be there all the time. If you need to call security, go to the nearest phone or call on your mobile: the number is 9666 and they will be with you as soon as they can.

The next thing I want to mention are your own personal security measures. By this I mean: the locks on your room door and window, your personal alarm and the university bus. All student rooms have a swipe lock that we open with our student cards – do not leave your room door unlocked if you are going out for a long period of time, and do not leave your card in a place where someone can pick it up and enter your room. This is, of course, common sense but people still leave their rooms unlocked and still leave their cards around. The next thing is your room window. Everyone has a key for their window and everyone should try to keep their windows locked when they are out of the building. However, the security guard has told me that he often finds windows open and even worse, he finds windows open on the ground floor. Please don't do this – it's an invitation to a burglar to enter the hall and take people's things.

Finally, two more items – personal alarms and the university bus. Now, the Students' Union gives every student their own personal alarm if you go to collect it. A personal alarm is something that gives out a loud noise if you press it when you think you may be in danger – it lets people know where you are and that you need help. The second thing you can do is use the university bus. It takes students from the campus to the town and to other places on campus. It goes every half an hour and it's free, so please try to use it, especially after dark.

## Track 14

| | |
|---|---|
| theft | thief |
| mugging | mugger |
| vandalism | vandal |
| shoplifting | shoplifter |
| truancy | truant |
| burglary | burglar |
| robbery | robber |
| crime | criminal |

# Unit 8

## Track 15

In today's lecture on international trade I'm going to look at the issue of protectionism. I'll start off with a definition of protectionism and then go on to look at the methods countries have used to protect their economy. Following this I'll look at the advantages and disadvantages of protectionism when compared to free and open trade.

So let's define protectionism. Protectionism at its simplest is the opposite of free trade, it is the practice of protecting domestic industries from foreign competition by using import duties or quotas. Options available to protect the economy are tariffs, embargos, subsidies and quotas. Let's examine these in turn with some examples.

Tariffs are one form of protectionism: it is a tax which is applied to imported goods but not to home-produced goods. The idea is to make the imported goods more expensive than the home-produced ones so that consumers buy home-produced items. An ongoing example of protectionism via tariff is between Britain and the USA.

Britain buys most of its bananas from Commonwealth countries largely in the Caribbean. However, the USA owns banana plantations in South America. In 1999, Britain refused to buy bananas from South America, so the US government put tariffs on some British-produced goods. The most famous example was a tariff of 100% import tax on wool products from Scotland brought into the United States.

The next method of protectionism is embargos. An embargo is a complete ban on the import of certain goods. For example, following the Cuban revolution in the 1950s, the USA banned the import of Cuban cigars. Unfortunately, Cuban cigars are the finest in the world and there is consequently a thriving black market in Cuban cigars in the USA. As we can see in the example, embargos can lead to a black market, or unofficial economy, if people want the goods badly enough.

Subsidies are a way governments support industries at home with money or tax breaks in order to allow them to compete better with foreign companies. In 1994 the French government provided its national airline with a £2 billion subsidy in order to help it compete with low-cost airlines. However, subsidies can have the effect of making home producers uncompetitive and inefficient.

Finally, let's look at quotas. A quota system allows a certain quantity of goods to be imported from other countries. The European Union has had quotas on textiles and clothing for decades to protect its textile industries from developing countries especially India and China. Understandably, developing countries say that this is unfair and against the principles of free trade.

Let's move on now to the arguments for and against protectionism. For trade to flourish between countries, the benefits from trade need to be equally balanced. Where a country feels that it is not getting a fair share of the trade, or that it is somehow disadvantaged, it might employ one or more of the methods of protection. There are at least four arguments that may be given for using protectionism. Firstly to protect employment in the home country. The simple view is that if imports are stopped, then jobs will be saved and even created at home. Secondly, to prevent unfair competition. It is often said that developing countries have the advantage of cheap labour costs in their countries and that they use this to undercut the price of the same goods produced in richer nations. A tariff might be applied to even out this imbalance. Thirdly, to protect new industries. A new industry, particularly one in a developing country, might not be able to compete with long-established industries elsewhere. Tariffs and quotas give new industries the chance to build up production to the point where they can compete. Fourthly, to raise money. Tariffs were once used as a way of raising revenue for the government. In modern countries they are now seldom used for this purpose, as the damage to trade often outweighs any immediate benefits.

Now for the arguments against protectionism, which are perhaps simpler to summarise. Although trade restrictions might help a country for a short period of time, their overall effect is a negative one. Restrictions affect the flow of trade, and the more countries employ restrictions, the less trade can flow. In the long run no one benefits from trade restriction because if one country puts restrictions on another country, the other country then puts their own restrictions on the first country. This affects the first country's exports and as the country finds it difficult to export goods, then unemployment is the result. So protection tends to help only the protected and can hide inefficient manufacturers.

# Track 16

1   Someone who takes money for a short time then returns it is called a borrower.

2   The committee, which meets every week, has elected a new treasurer.

3   The shares that I bought in February have gone up in value.

4   The company, which is based in Germany, has closed its factory in Indonesia.

5   Takashi, who I met at University, now trades in stocks and shares.

# Unit 9

## Track 17

And now to the final item in this evening's news. Captain Hanadi Hindi is the very first woman to become a professional pilot in Saudi Arabia. She has been awarded a ten-year contract to fly private jets, as announced by the Kingdom Holding company's chairman, Prince Alwaleed Bin Talal. The Prince is a 47-year-old self-made billionaire, nephew of the King, who is an advocate of women's rights and has called for a range of reforms to traditional Saudi society. Hindi's appointment is made all the more interesting because, in Saudi Arabia, women traditionally lead very sheltered lives.

In an interview, Captain Hanadi remarked, 'Women are capable of taking on any job previously monopolised by men.' She received her training at the Mid-east Aviation Academy in Amman, Jordan, where she studied flying with two other women and 70 men. She said that at first she found it difficult to adapt to life in Jordan, after a sheltered upbringing in the family home in Mecca. Her flight instructor, Mahmoud Aldour, confirmed that Hindi appeared shy and isolated when she first arrived. 'But now, I can make my own decisions,' she told reporters on the runway at Marka airport. Prince Alwaleed commented, 'I see this as a historic move for Saudi women,' and stated that he was in full support of women working in all areas.

Captain Hanadi comes from a family of four sisters and two brothers. She is the third sister, and the only one who is not married. She studied English Literature at university, but she decided to leave before graduating and went to study aviation. She has a Commercial Pilot's Licence and her picture was displayed at the Air Force Museum in Riyadh, showing that her position as the country's first woman pilot has received official recognition. 'I have my father and Prince Alwaleed to thank for this,' said Captain Hanadi. She added that becoming a pilot had been a lifelong dream which she shared with her father, but her mother was very reluctant to allow her to go to Jordan. 'Some of my friends were in

favour, some were against the career I chose,' she said.

Although she says that she can understand why women in Saudi Arabia are not allowed to drive, she believes that flying is different. In fact, working women are increasingly taking senior posts in universities, hospitals, banks and private companies. Captain Hanadi sums up her attitude to women's career opportunities in the country by saying, 'Women in Saudi Arabia can – given the chance – compete head on and excel.' However, she does not believe in changing her view that 'A woman is still a woman and she can never be like a man.'

## Track 18

management

performance

educational

applicant

university

resources

commission

prejudice

interpersonal

# Unit 10

## Track 19

**Presenter:** Good afternoon listeners, today on *Farmer's Market* I'll be talking to Barry and Sheila Watts, from Mildura, Australia. Good afternoon to you both.

**Sheila:** Hi.

**Barry:** G'day Phil.

**Presenter:** Now, back in 1997 you were one of the first farms in

Australia to go organic. Now you're one of the biggest producers in the state of Victoria. Tell us why you decided that growing organic vegetables and raising organic animals was the way forward, Barry?

**Barry:** Right. Well, back in the late 90s people were starting to get worried about GM foods and there was a lot of interest in alternatives, and in protecting the environment generally. Although our property was mainly a sheep farm, the wife's always been keen on growing vegetables and she had quite a good little business going on in the local markets.

**Sheila:** Yes, then one day this woman said to me, 'Are these tomatoes organically grown?', and I had to ask her, 'What do you mean by that?' She told me that organic veggies are grown without using chemicals such as pesticides, and that they were therefore safer and healthier to eat. She said it was a lifestyle thing, and that more and more people were insisting that all their food was organic, and they were prepared to pay more for it. That's when I got really interested, and decided to find out more about it.

**Barry:** We contacted the Biological Farmers' Association – that became the ACO or Australian Certified Organic in 2002 – and they told us there's a one-year pre-certification period during which you have to prepare the land for organic production.

**Presenter:** And how does that happen?

**Sheila:** The first step is soil preparation. I had to rip out all my crops and compost the lot, then dig over the three-hectare plot with the tractor. At the same time, we dug in organic fertiliser, compost and rock powder to improve the soil, and found suppliers of seed which met the standard set by the BFA.

**Barry:** After that we had our first visit from the inspectors, who let us know that we were on the right track, but it was another three years before we got certification to use the Bud logo.

**Presenter:** The Bud logo?

**Barry:** Yes, the logo shows the consumer that the supplier has been approved by the ACO. They know they can trust the food to be fair dinkum.

**Sheila:** After that, the business just took off. We went from three hectares to five, then to ten, now we have 50 in total, including the cow field and barn. Demand is greater than supply, so next year we're planning an orchard for plums, cherries and oranges.

**Presenter:** So, how do you manage without chemicals?

**Sheila:** It's all down to careful planning and crop rotation. That means, you move your vegetables to a different place each year, so if you have pests that attack cabbage and cauliflower, they don't have a chance to get established. Also, some plants like potatoes stop weeds from growing, so the following year you can plant your carrots and parsley there. It also helps you to get the most out of the soil.

**Presenter:** I reckon the organic farm must take up most of your time now, Barry. What about the sheep?

**Barry:** Yeah, the sheep used to subsidise the vegetables, now the veggies pay for the sheep. Well, we've decided to go organic with the sheep now, haven't we Sheila?

**Sheila:** Yes, We're going to breed them for meat, not wool, starting next year.

**Presenter:** Well, good luck to you. Thanks for coming in, Barry and Sheila Watts.

**Barry:** A pleasure.

**Sheila:** Thank you.

## Track 20

one of the first farms
one of the biggest producers
she told me that
and found suppliers of seed
we were on the right track

# Unit 11

## Track 21

**Presenter:** Do you think that climate change has nothing to do with you? Well, think again. Here to tell us more about how we contribute to climate change and what we can do about it is Professor Michael Stubbs from Edinburgh University. Hello, Michael.

**Michael Stubbs:** Hello there. Yes, climate change is everything to do with us! Most greenhouse emissions are a result of the decisions we make as individuals. But we can all take steps to stop climate change by reducing the amount of energy we use. In fact, you may have heard of the 'one-tonne challenge'. This is a project in Canada which aims to persuade the population to reduce their personal greenhouse emissions.

**Presenter:** What changes can we make in the way we live?

**Michael Stubbs:** Well, let's think about our homes and how we can cut back on the energy we use. Now the average house in the US and Australia generates eleven tonnes of greenhouses gases a year, with UK households generating about six tonnes a year. And most of that comes from heating and cooling. So, we need to dress suitably when we're at home. This means not wearing a T-shirt at home when it's snowing outside – we need to dress warmly instead. So, putting on more clothes when it is cold can help to reduce emissions. Now, home electrical appliances and lighting also use up a lot of energy. They together account for four tonnes of greenhouse gas emissions in the average Australian household and about two tonnes in a UK household. So choose the most efficient models of fridges and televisions and low-energy light bulbs. And don't leave your television on standby – unplug it altogether! In the US alone, standby power is responsible for 30 million tonnes of greenhouse emissions each year.

**Presenter:** Now what about all the rubbish we throw away?

**Michael Stubbs:** Well, here in Britain we throw away 27 million tonnes of rubbish from our homes every year. We get rid of anything from old drink cans to newspapers and plastic bags.

**Presenter:** So what happens to it all?

**Michael Stubbs:** Well, basically, it is either buried or burnt. Both these methods, of course, damage our environment. And most of our rubbish could be reused or recycled.

**Presenter**: So how can we start recycling?

**Michael Stubbs**: Well, taking all those empty glass bottles to your local bottle bank is a good way to begin. All glass collected from recycling banks is recycled back into bottles and jars. So every single glass bottle you deposit can help to reverse climate change. Now, there are separate banks for brown, green and clear glass. If you have blue glass this can be put into the green glass bank. Remember to remove all metal lids and plastic tops before recycling. And, some drinks bottles are covered in coloured plastic labels so be sure to remove them too. And avoid putting light bulbs or drinking glasses into bottle banks. They are not suitable for recycling because they require much higher temperatures than that needed for bottle glass.

**Presenter**: What about paper? Can all our junk mail and newspapers be recycled in paper banks?

**Michael Stubbs**: Yes, of course, but remember not to include envelopes as the glue used for sealing interferes with the recycling process. The same applies to books, either hard back or soft back because of the glue used to bind them. If you need to get rid of books and magazines, remember that libraries and charity shops will be happy to accept them.

**Presenter**: And what about mobile phones?

**Michael Stubbs**: Well, in fact, here in Edinburgh, we've got a 'Take Back' scheme where you can deposit handsets, batteries and chargers at recycling points in a number of electrical stores. Some charity shops also take unwanted phones to raise money.

## Track 22

1  so, global, ecosystem, ocean

2  more, resource, storm, warming

3  but, flood, hurricane, government

4  job, conservation, policy

# Unit 12

## Track 23

Hello there everyone, and welcome to our second session on interview skills. Now we have already looked at what to say in the interview and what to wear so let's consider non-verbal behaviour or, as it is more often called, body language. Believe it or not, research has shown that this is what makes the strongest impression on people we meet. Frequent eye contact is one aspect of body language which goes down very well with interviewers and creates a good impression. Looking at people means that you are sure of yourself and confident. In fact, one famous car company even makes a note of the level of eye contact candidates make during their recruitment process for this very reason. So, it is very important to maintain eye contact, but be careful how you do it! Avoid staring as this is a sign of hostility. But avoiding eye contact altogether and looking away or down is even worse! But the general message is maintain that eye contact. Believe me, the eyes have it!

Now, along with eye contact, smiling is one of the other important non-verbal actions which say more to the interviewer than any answers you give. A good way to create a good impression during the first few minutes of your interview is to smile warmly when you meet the person or people who will be interviewing you. It shows them that you are relaxed. Facial scanning takes a triangular route from the eyes down to the mouth and back to the eyes. Even when you aren't speaking, an interviewer will be noticing your mouth so give a relaxed smile whenever you feel it is appropriate.

Now, not surprisingly, interviewers pay most attention to a person's face or head during an interview. And they certainly pick up a lot on what they see. Researchers have identified nodding as going down very well with interviewers. This simple gesture shows that you are listening and paying attention. Another useful head gesture is to tilt your head slightly to one side. Now this reinforces that you are listening well to what the interviewer is saying to you. However, tilting your head back isn't such a good idea as this signals arrogance. And drooping your head forward indicates that you are lacking in confidence. And as we all know, that is exactly the opposite of what an interviewer wants to see! So the message is – mind your head!

Now posture – or the way that you carry yourself – is an important area of body language to be aware of. And it is one of the first body language signals that interviewers read as you enter a room. Posture also matters when you are sitting down. A well-supported position with your shoulders square and sitting full back on the chair will give the impression that you are confident which is just what the interviewer wants to see. I once interviewed a candidate who perched right on the edge of her chair throughout. I kept feeling that she was about to run out of the room in terror! However, occasionally leaning forward slightly when the interviewer is speaking reinforces the message that you are keen and interested, as well as showing the interviewer that you are actually listening to what they are saying. But don't overdo it by leaning too far forward. That can be a bit distracting for the interviewer!

Now we all tend to use our hands to gesture – especially when we are explaining something or as we become involved in what we are saying. This is fine. It shows that we are keen and perhaps even excited about something. However, what can work against someone at an interview is when they fidget. This kind of moving about is of course what we do when we are nervous and fidgeting can be very distracting to watch. So if this is a problem for you when you get nervous, it is a good idea to practise sitting with your hands gently resting in your lap or on the arms of the chair. Try not to fold your arms though as this tends to look uncomfortable or hostile. But whatever movements you make, be careful with your hands. They need to be kept well away from your mouth, head or face. In fact, experts say that when a hand flies up to or over a person's mouth it implies that the person is worried or wound up about something.

For most of us, staying calm in an interview situation is a challenge so putting in a bit of practice in advance will help. So, to end with, here are a couple of suggestions on how to improve our body language. A good idea is to choose a role model such as an actor or fictional character or a public figure or someone you know. Then sit calmly and imagine that you are this person. Now, other countries have different body language signals. So, remember that if you are being interviewed abroad, you may want to check if there are any special gestures to avoid. It is also a good idea to get used to reading body language signals. You can do this by simply watching how people interact in public places such as on the streets or in restaurants. And finally, when people have struck up a rapport it is reflected through the natural mirroring of each other's body language movements. So, you can use this to your advantage by occasionally mirroring the interviewer's own movements. For example, if they lean over to one side, you can do the same a few seconds later. It helps to create a special effect known as 'similar to me'. But don't do it too often or the interviewer will notice! Now any questions before we move on to interview listening skills?

## Track 24

| | | | |
|---|---|---|---|
| 1 | interested | 8 | graduation |
| 2 | delightful | 9 | wonderful |
| 3 | farewell | 10 | ceremony |
| 4 | petrifying | 11 | invitation |
| 5 | enjoyable | 12 | milk round |
| 6 | barbecue | 13 | challenging |
| 7 | boring | 14 | wound up |

New College Nottingham
Learning Centres